D1415591

THE JEWISH
PUZZLE BOOK

FOR THE ENTIRE FAMILY

THE JEWISH PUZZLE BOOK

FOR THE ENTIRE FAMILY

Sylvia & Arthur Levinsohn

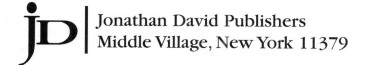

JD | Jonathan David Publishers
Middle Village, New York 11379

THE JEWISH PUZZLE BOOK

Copyright © 1995
by
Sylvia & Arthur Levinsohn

No part of this book may be reproduced without
the written permission of the publishers.
Address all inquiries to:

Jonathan David Publishers, Inc.
68-22 Eliot Avenue
Middle Village, New York 11379

ISBN 0-8246-0379-6

Book design by Rodney Jung
Printed in the United States of America

To our dear grandaughters,
Jessica Carli and Abby Levinsohn,
wishing you joy and pride
in your Jewish heritage.

Before Beginning...

In *The Jewish Puzzle Book*, you will find crosswords, scrambled words, acrostics, word searches, and other puzzles based on Jewish themes. We hope that everyone in your family will find these puzzles challenging, educational, and, of course, entertaining.

The puzzles are arranged in order of difficulty. Youngsters will be able to solve the puzzles on the earlier pages while adults will enjoy the later ones. So now take pencil in hand (and perhaps an eraser), and proceed with the challenge. A hearty *mazel tov* to all who complete them!

Bear in mind that some of the Hebrew words used in the puzzles are transliterated in more than one way. The following list will serve as a guide in your puzzle-solving.

ADAR	CHOLENT	MENORA
ADIR HU	DRAYDEL, DREIDEL	MITZVAH
AFIKOMON	EIN GEDI	MUSAF AMIDA
AHASUEROS	ELUL	NEILA
AKDAMUT	GIMMEL	NEROT
AL CHET	HAFTARA	ONEG SHABBAT
AL HANISIM	HAGGADA	ROSH HASHANA
ALIYA	HALVAH	SHALACHMONES
ALIYOT	HAMANTASHEN	SHALOM ALEICHEM
ASHAMNU	HAMANTASCHEN	SHAMASH
ATZERET	HAMOTZI	SHEHECHEYANU
AVINU MALKENU	HAVDALA	SHEM
AYTZ CHAYYIM	HINENI	SHEV ARIM
AYSHET CHAYIL	JAPHETH	SHANKBONE
BIRKAT HAMAZON	KASHA VARNISHKES	SHTREIMELS
BORSCHT	KICHEL	SIDRA
CHAD GADYA	KITTEL	TALIT
CHAG HABIKURIM	LECHA DODI	TEKIA
CHAG SAMEACH	LESHANA TOVA	TISHRI
CHALLA	MAKRI	TORA, TORAH
CHALLOT	MALCHUYOT	TZIMMES
CHAMETZ	MATZA	YARMULKA, YARMULKE
CHASSIDIM	MEGILLA, MEGILLAH	YOM HADIN
CHANUKA	MEGILLAT	ZERESH
CHAROSET	MEGILLOT	ZICHRONOT

PUZZLES

Fill in the blank spaces with the letters below. The filled-in letters
will form a Bible quotation.

THE GOLDEN RULE

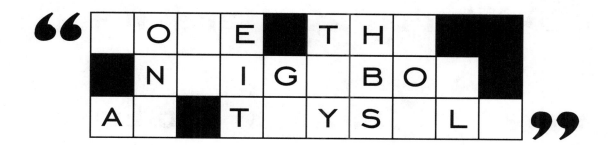

"
V Y E R S

H E F H L
"

Rebus

THE BROTHERS

For solution see page 76

Bible Quote

Fill in the blank spaces with the letters below. The filled-in letters will form a Bible quotation.

FAITH IN GOD

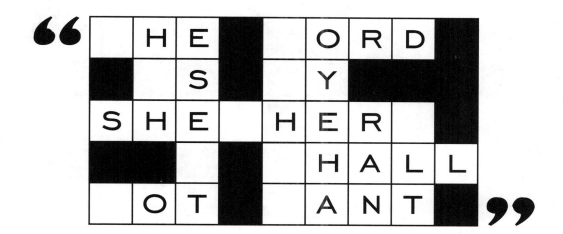

" WITLD

MISPN "

Acrostic

Find the appropriate answer to the clues listed and write the word in the numbered spaces to the right. Then transfer each letter to the corresponding numbered box in the diagram above. When done correctly, one or more sentences relating to the subject of the puzzle will be formed.

Afikomon

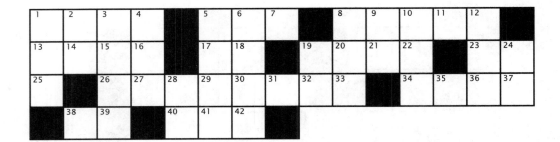

1	2	3	4		5	6	7		8	9	10	11	12	
13	14	15	16		17	18		19	20	21	22		23	24
25		26	27	28	29	30	31	32	33		34	35	36	37
	38	39		40	41	42								

1. Swallow liquid

2. Belonging to me

3. Avoid; ignore

4. Opposite of black

5. Sum of money

6. Inn

7. Baseball Hall of _____

8. It's between your eyes

9. There was an old lady who lived in a _____

10. What you do at lunch

1. ___ ___ ___ ___ ___
   10 12 38 33 29

2. ___ ___ ___ ___
   31 17 36 9

3. ___ ___ ___ ___
   39 6 35 21

4. ___ ___ ___ ___ ___
   1 34 28 23 14

5. ___ ___ ___ ___
   27 41 42 19

6. ___ ___ ___ ___ ___
   24 20 37 3 16

7. ___ ___ ___ ___
   40 26 13 7

8. ___ ___ ___ ___
   4 32 8 22

9. ___ ___ ___ ___
   18 2 30 11

10. ___ ___ ___
    25 15 5

For solution see page 77

Rebus

ANCIENT ENEMY

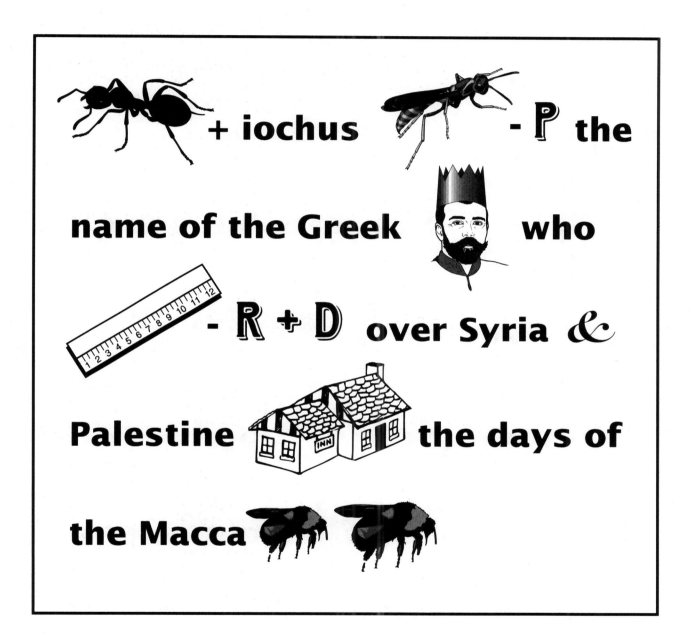

+ iochus   - P the

name of the Greek   who

- R + D over Syria &

Palestine   the days of

the Macca

Word Search

Search the puzzle for the words listed alongside it. As you find each word,
circle it or draw a line through it. The words may be spelled forward or
backward and may appear horizontally, vertically, diagonally, or even around
the outer corners of the puzzle.

A TEMPLE MIRACLE

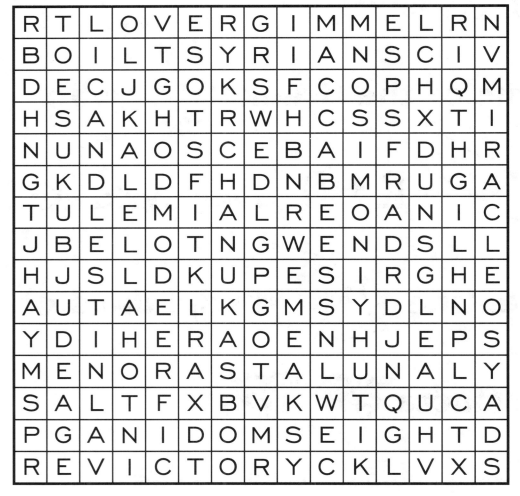

R	T	L	O	V	E	R	G	I	M	M	E	L	R	N
B	O	I	L	T	S	Y	R	I	A	N	S	C	I	V
D	E	C	J	G	O	K	S	F	C	O	P	H	Q	M
H	S	A	K	H	T	R	W	H	C	S	S	X	T	I
N	U	N	A	O	S	C	E	B	A	I	F	D	H	R
G	K	D	L	D	F	H	D	N	B	M	R	U	G	A
T	U	L	E	M	I	A	L	R	E	O	A	N	I	C
J	B	E	L	O	T	N	G	W	E	N	D	S	L	L
H	J	S	L	D	K	U	P	E	S	I	R	G	H	E
A	U	T	A	E	L	K	G	M	S	Y	D	L	N	O
Y	D	I	H	E	R	A	O	E	N	H	J	E	P	S
M	E	N	O	R	A	S	T	A	L	U	N	A	L	Y
S	A	L	T	F	X	B	V	K	W	T	Q	U	C	A
P	G	A	N	I	D	O	M	S	E	I	G	H	T	D
R	E	V	I	C	T	O	R	Y	C	K	L	V	X	S

CANDLES
CHANUKA
DREIDEL
EIGHT DAYS
FREEDOM
GELT
GIMMEL
HALLEL
HAY
JUDAH
JUDEA
LIGHT
MACCABEES
MENORA
MIRACLE
MODIN
NEROT
NUN
OIL
REVOLT
ROCK OF AGES
SHAMASH
SHIN
SIMON
SYRIANS
VICTORY

For solution see page 78

Bible Stories

Fill in the blank spaces with the correct letters, then read the filled-in letters from top to bottom to discover an appropriate title for this puzzle.

EV __

SERPE __ T

A __ AM

DIS __ BEYED

__ IG LEAF

EX __ ELLED

CRE __ TION

WA __ NING

G __ RDEN

FORBI __ DEN

FRU __ T

CA __ T OUT

ED __ N

For solution see page 79

Fill in the blank spaces with the letters below. The filled-in letters
will form a Bible quotation.

CAIN'S QUESTION

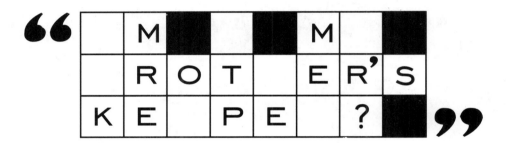

"

	M				M	
	R	O	T		E	R'S
K	E		P	E		?

"

I Y H

E A B R

For solution see page 79

Acrostic

Find the appropriate answer to the clues listed and write the word in the numbered spaces to the right. Then transfer each letter to the corresponding numbered box in the diagram above. When done correctly, one or more sentences relating to the subject of the puzzle will be formed.

Daniel

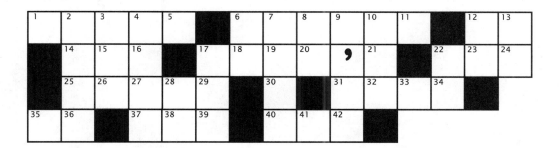

1. E.T.

2. Fair-haired

3. Angel's residence

4. Revolve, spin

5. Royal seat

6. Boring, blunt

7. Stormy

8. Slender

1. ___ ___ ___ ___ ___
   37   11   12   5   20

2. ___ ___ ___ ___ ___ ___
   1   38   19   8   22   16

3. ___ ___ ___ ___ ___ ___
   31   32   30   4   10   13

4. ___ ___ ___ ___ ___ ___
   26   34   14   3   35   23

5. ___ ___ ___ ___ ___ ___
   25   15   33   36   24   41

6. ___ ___ ___ ___
   6   27   17   39

7. ___ ___ ___ ___ ___
   2   7   18   42   29

8. ___ ___ ___ ___
   21   28   9   40

Scrambled Words

Rearrange the letters below and fill in the blanks to form
words that relate to the title of the puzzle.

ESCAPE FROM SLAVERY

1. PEGTY   _ _ _ _ _
2. AZMAT   _ _ _ _ _
3. SUEDOX   _ _ _ _ _ _
4. REEDS   _ _ _ _ _
5. FOAMNIKO   _ _ _ _ _ _ _ _
6. MATCHEZ   _ _ _ _ _ _ _
7. DACH DAYAG   _ _ _ _ _ _ _ _ _
8. TOSEARCH   _ _ _ _ _ _ _ _
9. RAISETILES   _ _ _ _ _ _ _ _ _ _
10. DAGAGAH   _ _ _ _ _ _ _
11. JAILHE   _ _ _ _ _ _
12. TRIBET BERSH   _ _ _ _ _ _ _ _ _ _ _
13. SAVEPROS   _ _ _ _ _ _ _ _

20

For solution see page 80

Acrostic

Find the appropriate answer to the clues listed and write the word in the numbered spaces to the right. Then transfer each letter to the corresponding numbered box in the diagram above. When done correctly, one or more sentences relating to the subject of the puzzle will be formed.

Jonah

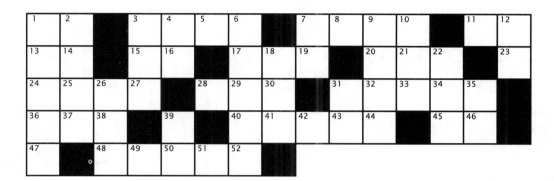

1. Greeting

2. Portion

3. Cereal

4. Chopped mixture

5. Error, failing

6. Past events

7. Merry, gay

8. Pineapple island

9. Mend

10. Twelve inches

11. Garden tool

1. ___ ___ ___ ___ ___
   8   2   43 18 50

2. ___ ___ ___ ___ ___
   48 35 39 51 12

3. ___ ___ ___ ___ ___
   23 30 37 5   16

4. ___ ___ ___ ___
   36 42 22 20

5. ___ ___ ___ ___
   46 24 17 40

6. ___ ___ ___ ___ ___ ___ ___
   3   21 10 49 29 13 27

7. ___ ___ ___ ___ ___
   31 14 19 6   52

8. ___ ___ ___ ___ ___ ___
   41 34 1   47 15 9

9. ___ ___ ___ ___
   38 4   26 33

10. ___ ___ ___ ___
    28 45 25 7

11. ___ ___ ___
    11 32 44

For solution see page 81

Word Search

Search the puzzle for the words listed alongside it. As you find each word, circle it or draw a line through it. The words may be spelled forward or backward and may appear horizontally, vertically, diagonally, or even around the outer corners of the puzzle.

HEARTBURN

L	E	D	H	E	R	R	I	N	G	S	E	K	H	S
K	N	E	E	S	E	H	S	I	N	K	B	I	G	I
C	A	L	L	A	H	C	R	T	S	K	O	C	H	N
I	M	D	E	R	M	A	E	H	R	S	R	H	U	R
P	T	C	H	A	L	K	V	E	L	E	S	E	B	A
U	H	D	W	X	S	E	P	E	V	I	C	L	L	V
O	A	Y	O	I	C	L	G	I	F	N	H	S	I	A
S	V	L	R	R	A	A	L	E	V	S	T	L	N	H
N	L	B	O	C	B	D	T	A	F	C	W	E	T	S
E	A	L	H	I	E	L	K	S	B	H	Y	D	Z	A
K	H	U	S	P	I	U	E	O	J	A	Q	U	E	K
C	A	R	P	F	G	K	N	D	Y	V	Z	R	S	R
I	F	O	E	E	T	S	E	A	N	P	J	T	V	O
H	H	G	L	A	N	E	L	D	N	A	M	S	A	T
C	H	O	L	E	N	T	T	Z	I	M	M	E	S	M

BAGELS
BLINTZES
BORSCHT
BRISKET
CARP
CHALLA
CHICKEN SOUP
CHOLENT
CHOPPED LIVER
DERMA
GEFILTE FISH
HALVAH
KASHA VARNISHKES
KICHEL
KNISHES
KREPLACH
KUGEL
LATKES
LEKACH
LOX
MANDELBRODT
MANDLEN
MATZA BALLS
PICKLED HERRING
PTCHA
SCHAV
STRUDEL
TZIMMES

For solution see page 81

Acrostic

Find the appropriate answer to the clues listed and write the word in the numbered spaces to the right. Then transfer each letter to the corresponding numbered box in the diagram above. When done correctly, one or more sentences relating to the subject of the puzzle will be formed.

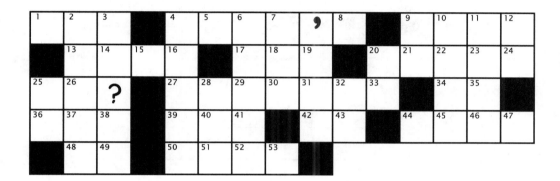

Cain

1. Shiver, tremble
2. Sheep's cry
3. Launder
4. Dark tan
5. Elevate
6. Swing back and forth
7. Home, shelter
8. "Uncle Tom's _____"
9. Frozen rain
10. Dirt-free
11. Custom, practice

1. __6__ __24__ __44__ __15__ __28__
2. __20__ __13__ __47__ __50__ __8__
3. __4__ __30__ __43__ __2__
4. __27__ __21__ __40__ __36__ __39__
5. __26__ __10__ __14__ __38__ __33__
6. __32__ __1__ __48__ __3__
7. __34__ __22__ __31__ __19__ __52__
8. __9__ __42__ __45__ __18__ __12__
9. __49__ __53__ __16__ __35__ __23__
10. __29__ __46__ __25__ __37__ __7__
11. __17__ __5__ __51__ __11__ __41__

For solution see page 82

Scrambled Words

Rearrange the letters below and fill in the blanks to form
words that relate to the title of the puzzle.

MARDI GRAS

1. COMRADEI   __ __ __ __ __ __ __ __
2. HSETER   __ __ __ __ __ __
3. LOWSLAG   __ __ __ __ __ __ __
4. NAVALRIC   __ __ __ __ __ __ __ __
5. SHIVAT   __ __ __ __ __ __
6. GORGERSG   __ __ __ __ __ __ __ __
7. ROSAHUESA   __ __ __ __ __ __ __ __ __
8. MANAH   __ __ __ __ __
9. STEMUCOS   __ __ __ __ __ __ __ __
10. ASPIRE   __ __ __ __ __ __
11. SHAMENATHAN   __ __ __ __ __ __ __ __ __ __ __
12. UPMIR   __ __ __ __ __
13. ONEIS   __ __ __ __ __

24

For solution see page 82

Word Search

Search the puzzle for the words listed alongside it. As you find each word, circle it or draw a line through it. The words may be spelled forward or backward and may appear horizontally, vertically, diagonally, or even around the outer corners of the puzzle.

A RESTFUL DAY

L	F	R	U	D	D	I	S	P	I	C	E	B	O	X
W	A	T	A	L	I	T	E	A	R	D	I	S	M	S
A	Y	M	J	T	O	L	L	A	H	C	L	E	D	N
H	S	U	D	D	I	K	D	Q	U	V	H	E	I	O
S	H	R	E	N	B	A	N	R	W	C	K	D	T	Z
R	E	I	Z	T	O	M	A	H	I	L	O	S	K	A
E	T	T	H	U	V	P	C	E	U	D	E	R	D	M
Y	C	F	A	C	I	T	L	M	A	R	E	A	A	A
A	H	A	V	K	O	A	R	H	M	R	N	B	Y	H
R	A	M	D	R	M	A	C	O	L	O	I	B	O	T
P	Y	J	A	O	Y	E	N	G	H	T	W	I	F	A
T	I	Z	L	B	L	E	S	S	I	N	G	S	R	K
Z	L	O	A	M	A	R	A	T	F	A	H	W	E	R
C	H	O	L	E	N	T	K	Q	J	C	I	F	S	I
S	T	I	O	N	E	G	S	H	A	B	B	A	T	B

AYSHET CHAYIL
BIRKAT HAMAZON
BLESSINGS
CANDLES
CANTOR
CHALLOT
CHOLENT
DAY OF REST
HAFTARA
HAMOTZI
HAVDALA
KIDDUSH
KIPA
LECHA DODI
MAFTIR
ONEG SHABBAT
PRAYERSHAWL
RABBIS
SERMON
SHALOM ALEICHEM
SIDDUR
SIDRA
SPICEBOX
TALIT
TORA
WINE
YARMULKE

Acrostic

Find the appropriate answer to the clues listed and write the word in the numbered spaces to the right. Then transfer each letter to the corresponding numbered box in the diagram above. When done correctly, one or more sentences relating to the subject of the puzzle will be formed.

Purim

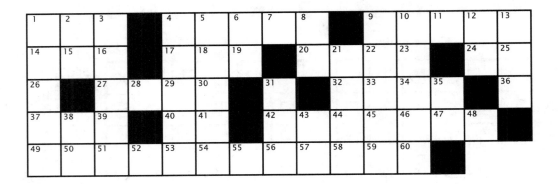

1. Almond; pecan

   1. ___ ___ ___
     60 25 39

2. Insect bite

   2. ___ ___ ___ ___ ___
     22 1 7 53 48

3. Noon meal

   3. ___ ___ ___ ___ ___
     16 5 47 57 45

4. Point a gun

   4. ___ ___ ___
     15 33 51

5. Mend; darn

   5. ___ ___ ___ ___ ___
     4 55 26 9 58

6. Skinny

   6. ___ ___ ___ ___
     54 17 40 12

7. What Red Riding Hood carried

   7. ___ ___ ___ ___ ___ ___
     36 52 19 34 3 30

8. Scrubs

   8. ___ ___ ___ ___ ___ ___
     27 10 56 2 21 38

9. It dines on wool

   9. ___ ___ ___ ___
     8 43 23 49

10. Bee's homes

  10. ___ ___ ___ ___ ___
     28 46 14 59 41

11. Roaring fire

  11. ___ ___ ___ ___ ___
     24 32 29 20 37

12. Dried grape

  12. ___ ___ ___ ___ ___ ___
     6 18 31 44 13 42

13. _____ of corn

  13. ___ ___ ___
     35 50 11

For solution see page 83

Bible Stories

Fill in the blank spaces with the correct letters, then read the filled-in
letters from top to bottom to discover an appropriate title for this puzzle.

S __ RONG

RED CO __ D

JOSH __ A

AM __ ORITES

__ ROMISED LAND

J __ RICHO

FAI __ H

COLLA __ SE

SHIL __ H

HIGH __ ALLS

TRIB __

DA __ ING

For solution see page 84

Acrostic

Find the appropriate answer to the clues listed and write the word in the numbered spaces to the right. Then transfer each letter to the corresponding numbered box in the diagram above. When done correctly, one or more sentences relating to the subject of the puzzle will be formed.

MUSCLE MAN

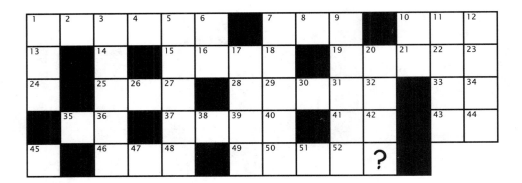

1. Spade

2. Take it with a _____ of salt

3. Gets together

4. French _____; _____ master

5. Love symbol

6. Adult female

7. Thick and spready

8. Performer

9. Cowboy's neckerchief

10. Carves; slices

1. ___ ___ ___ ___ ___ ___
   10 38 46 15 42 31

2. ___ ___ ___ ___ ___
   24 50 47 33 6

3. ___ ___ ___ ___ ___
   3 36 16 48 19

4. ___ ___ ___ ___ ___
   37 22 26 1 44

5. ___ ___ ___ ___ ___
   41 45 8 21 34

6. ___ ___ ___ ___ ___
   7 5 25 51 23

7. ___ ___ ___ ___ ___
   49 30 4 13 18

8. ___ ___ ___ ___ ___
   14 12 40 29 17

9. ___ ___ ___ ___ ___ ___ ___
   35 43 27 32 2 52 39

10. ___ ___ ___ ___
    28 11 20 9

For solution see page 84

Crossword

Fill in the blank spaces from left to right using the clues provided.

Winter Holiday

1. Liberty, independence
2. Spinning top
3. Courageous fighters
4. Caretaker
5. Potato pancakes
6. Candelabrum
7. Presents
8. Wax tapers
9. Lighting fluid
10. A week plus one (2 words)
11. December festival
12. Yiddish money
13. Middle East enemies

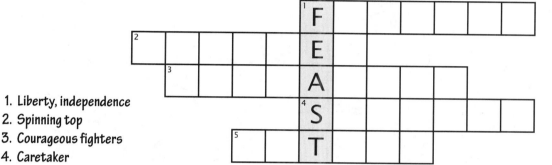

Acrostic

Find the appropriate answer to the clues listed and write the word in the numbered spaces to the right. Then transfer each letter to the corresponding numbered box in the diagram above. When done correctly, one or more sentences relating to the subject of the puzzle will be formed.

JOSHUA

1. Small bird, gulp

1. ___ ___ ___ ___ ___ ___ ___
   19 40 10 37 24 54   1

2. Leaped

2. ___ ___ ___ ___ ___ ___
   5   21 22 16 47 26

3. Locate

3. ___ ___ ___ ___
   48 30 58 59

4. Courageous

4. ___ ___ ___ ___ ___ ___
   46 25 13 33 43 31

5. Amble

5. ___ ___ ___ ___ ___ ___
   42 12 50   6 38 63

6. Boast

6. ___ ___ ___ ___ ___ ___ ___
   23 62 14 39 52   3 60

7. Brief

7. ___ ___ ___ ___ ___
   51   2 61 29 20

8. Express gratitude

8. ___ ___ ___ ___ ___
   18   8 36   4 56

9. Dry grass

9. ___ ___ ___ ___ ___
   11 45 53 57 35

10. Righteousness

10. ___ ___ ___ ___ ___ ___ ___
    27   9 34 44 49 55 17

11. Disgrace

11. ___ ___ ___ ___ ___
    7   32 41 15 28

For solution see page 85

Bible Stories

Fill in the blank spaces with the correct letters, then read the filled-in letters from top to bottom to discover an appropriate title for this puzzle.

___ OSEPH

M ___ NY

___ OLORED

C ___ AT

FORCI ___ LY

EN ___ LAVED

TROU ___ LED

DR ___ AMS

___ OLD TO

PO ___ IPHAR

___ EVEN

GO ___ D YEARS

LEA ___ YEARS

Word Search

Search the puzzle for the words listed alongside it. As you find each word, circle it or draw a line through it. The words may be spelled forward or backward and may appear horizontally, vertically, diagonally, or even around the outer corners of the puzzle.

LIBERTY

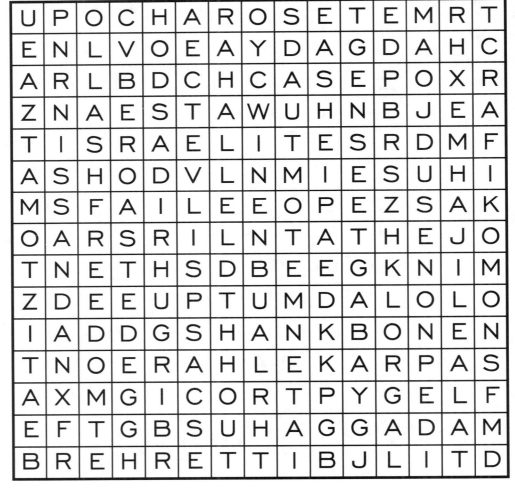

U	P	O	C	H	A	R	O	S	E	T	E	M	R	T
E	N	L	V	O	E	A	Y	D	A	G	D	A	H	C
A	R	L	B	D	C	H	C	A	S	E	P	O	X	R
Z	N	A	E	S	T	A	W	U	H	N	B	J	E	A
T	I	S	R	A	E	L	I	T	E	S	R	D	M	F
A	S	H	O	D	V	L	N	M	I	E	S	U	H	I
M	S	F	A	I	L	E	E	O	P	E	Z	S	A	K
O	A	R	S	R	I	L	N	T	A	T	H	E	J	O
T	N	E	T	H	S	D	B	E	E	G	K	N	I	M
Z	D	E	E	U	P	T	U	M	D	A	L	O	L	O
I	A	D	D	G	S	H	A	N	K	B	O	N	E	N
T	N	O	E	R	A	H	L	E	K	A	R	P	A	S
A	X	M	G	I	C	O	R	T	P	Y	G	E	L	F
E	F	T	G	B	S	U	H	A	G	G	A	D	A	M
B	R	E	H	R	E	T	T	I	B	J	L	I	T	D

ADIR HU
AFIKOMON
BITTER HERB
CHAD GADYA
CHAMETZ
CHAROSET
EGYPT
ELIJAH
EXODUS
FREEDOM
HAGGADA
HALLEL
ISRAELITES
KARPAS
MATZA
MOTZI
NISSAN
PESACH
RED SEA
ROASTED EGG
SEDER
SHANKBONE
UNLEAVENED BREAD
WINE

For solution see page 86

Acrostic

Find the appropriate answer to the clues listed and write the word in the numbered spaces to the right. Then transfer each letter to the corresponding numbered box in the diagram above. When done correctly, one or more sentences relating to the subject of the puzzle will be formed.

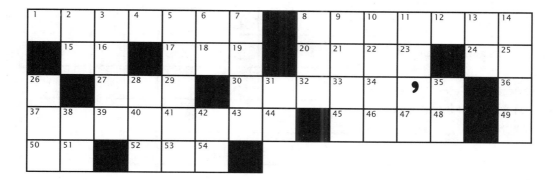

Goliath

1	2	3	4	5	6	7		8	9	10	11	12	13	14
	15	16		17	18	19		20	21	22	23		24	25
26		27	28	29		30	31	32	33	34	,	35		36
37	38	39	40	41	42	43	44		45	46	47	48		49
50	51		52	53	54									

1. Nanny, not a nursemaid

2. Remove whiskers

3. Join, become one

4. Flare of light

5. Seethe, become agitated

6. Pulverized earth

7. Sun _____ tomatoes

8. Small horse

9. Post office delivery

10. Suggestions, clues

11. Move smoothly

12. Display, entertainment

1. ___ ___ ___ ___
   40 53 15 6

2. ___ ___ ___ ___ ___
   8   42 46 32 13

3. ___ ___ ___ ___ ___
   28 22 33 44 10

4. ___ ___ ___ ___ ___
   24 3   31 41 17

5. ___ ___ ___ ___
   27 2   38 52

6. ___ ___ ___ ___
   14 21 19 29

7. ___ ___ ___ ___ ___
   30 12 47 26 48

8. ___ ___ ___ ___
   20 43 9   23

9. ___ ___ ___ ___
   51 5   18 37

10. ___ ___ ___ ___ ___
    49 4   39 16 35

11. ___ ___ ___ ___ ___
    1   45 50 34 11

12. ___ ___ ___ ___
    36 7   25 54

For solution see page 87

(33)

Crossword

Fill in the blank spaces from left to right using the clues provided.

Jewish Laws

1. Famous laws were written on _____ (2 words)
2. Agreement
3. The laws were given here (2 words)
4. Idol (2 words)

5. Great Jewish leader
6. Recall
7. Unleavened bread
8. Disasters
9. Biblical flaming shrub (2 words)
10. Colorful body of water (2 words)
11. Commandments
12. Flight departure
13. Lord alone (2 words)
14. Predictor
15. Religious practice

The down answer spells: TEN COMMANDMENTS

For solution see page 87

Bible Quote

Fill in the blank spaces with the letters below. The filled-in letters
will form a Bible quotation.

REPUTATION ABOVE ALL

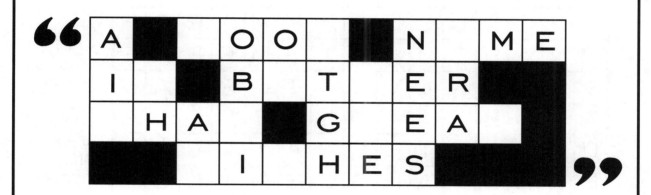

"

A	■		O	O		■	N		M	E
I		■	B		T		E	R	■	■
	H	A		■	G		E	A		■
■				I		H	E	S	■	■

"

D A S T E N

G T C R R T

Word Search

Search the puzzle for the words listed alongside it. As you find each word, circle it or draw a line through it. The words may be spelled forward or backward and may appear horizontally, vertically, diagonally, or even around the outer corners of the puzzle.

A Queen's Triumph

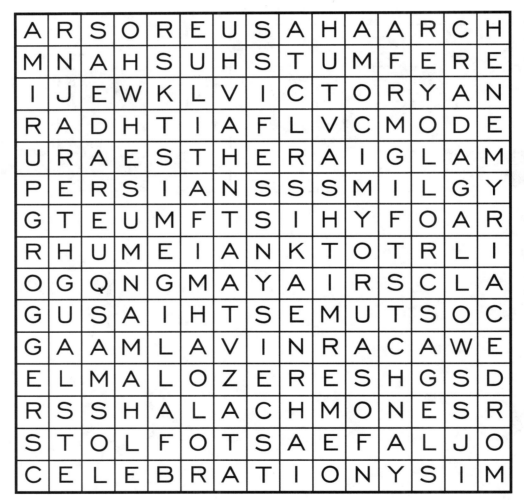

A	R	S	O	R	E	U	S	A	H	A	A	R	C	H
M	N	A	H	S	U	H	S	T	U	M	F	E	R	E
I	J	E	W	K	L	V	I	C	T	O	R	Y	A	N
R	A	D	H	T	I	A	F	L	V	C	M	O	D	E
U	R	A	E	S	T	H	E	R	A	I	G	L	A	M
P	E	R	S	I	A	N	S	S	S	M	I	L	G	Y
G	T	E	U	M	F	T	S	I	H	Y	F	O	A	R
R	H	U	M	E	I	A	N	K	T	O	T	R	L	I
O	G	Q	N	G	M	A	Y	A	I	R	S	C	L	A
G	U	S	A	I	H	T	S	E	M	U	T	S	O	C
G	A	A	M	L	A	V	I	N	R	A	C	A	W	E
E	L	M	A	L	O	Z	E	R	E	S	H	G	S	D
R	S	S	H	A	L	A	C	H	M	O	N	E	S	R
S	T	O	L	F	O	T	S	A	E	F	A	L	J	O
C	E	L	E	B	R	A	T	I	O	N	Y	S	I	M

ADAR
AHASUEROS
ALHANISIM
ARCHENEMY
CARNIVAL
CELEBRATION
COSTUMES
ESTHER
FAITH
FEAST OF LOTS
GALLOWS
GIFTS
GROGGERS
HAMAN
HAMANTASHEN
MASQUERADE
MASSACRE
MEGILLA
MORDECAI
PERSIANS
PURIM
SHALACHMONES
SCROLL
SHUSHAN
SLAUGHTER
VASHTI
VICTORY
ZERESH

For solution see page 88

Bible Stories

Fill in the blank spaces with the correct letters, then read the filled-in
letters from top to bottom to discover an appropriate title for this puzzle.

INTRE __ ID

DANIE __

L __ ONS DEN

KIN __ DARIUS

UN __ ARMED

HANDWRI __ ING

JEAL __ USY

__ IERY

FURN __ CE

MES __ ACH

AB __ D-NEGO

SHAD __ ACH

C __ URAGEOUS

For solution see page 89

Acrostic

Find the appropriate answer to the clues listed and write the word in the numbered spaces to the right. Then transfer each letter to the corresponding numbered box in the diagram above. When done correctly, one or more sentences relating to the subject of the puzzle will be formed.

Bridegroom

1		2	3	4		5	6	7	8	9	10	11		12
13		14		15	16	17	18	19		20	21	22	23	24
25	26	27		28	29	30		31	32		33		34	35
36	37	38	39	40		41	42	43	44		45	46	47	
48	49	50	51	52	53	54	55	56	57		58	59	60	61
62	63	64		65		66	67	68	69	70		71	72	73
74		75	76	77		78	79	80	81					

1. Beast
2. Bad guy (slang); headgear
3. Scouts aim for merit _____
4. Craft for making sweaters
5. Breezy
6. Earnings
7. Good physical shape
8. Safecracker
9. Grin
10. What poison ivy makes you do
11. Crusty fruit pastries
12. Beat; won out
13. One who gives a party
14. Roll with a hole

1. __ __ __ __ __ __
   33 21 14 57 65 77

2. __ __ __ __
   42 55 7 37

3. __ __ __ __ __ __
   15 75 51 2 35 69

4. __ __ __ __ __ __ __ __
   19 39 25 71 4 12 44 66

5. __ __ __ __ __
   41 38 26 11 22

6. __ __ __ __ __
   34 18 53 47 5

7. __ __ __ __ __ __ __
   62 10 31 67 45 24 74

8. __ __ __ __ __ __ __
   48 29 54 27 8 80 16

9. __ __ __ __ __
   61 59 1 79 17

10. __ __ __ __ __ __ __
    58 6 49 20 32 78 46

11. __ __ __ __
    81 50 73 64

12. __ __ __ __ __ __ __ __
    36 63 13 3 68 30 43 9

13. __ __ __ __
    72 56 70 23

14. __ __ __ __ __
    28 60 40 52 76

For solution see page 89

Scrambled Words

Rearrange the letters below and fill in the blanks to form
words that relate to the title of the puzzle.

Celebrate With Lights

1. STEALK — — — — — — —

2. CORK FO SAGE — — — — — — — — — — — — —

3. CAMEBACES — — — — — — — — —

4. REDLIED — — — — — — —

5. MOANER — — — — — —

6. SAMHASH — — — — — — —

7. ACTIONHSU — — — — — — — — —

8. SINRAYS — — — — — — —

9. HETIG SYDA — — — — — — — — —

10. ACTINODIED — — — — — — — — — —

11. SERPENTS — — — — — — — —

12. TITLEK — — — — — —

13. HACANUK — — — — — — —

For solution see page 90

39

Diagram

CHANUKA

ACROSS:

1. Hasmonean brother
3. Brave soldiers
6. Money in Yiddish
7. Israeli southern kingdom
9. Leader of number 3 above

DOWN:

2. Divine event
3. Candelabrum
4. Syrian-Greek king
5. Blessing over the first fruits
8. The leading candle

Scrambled Words

Rearrange the letters below and fill in the blanks to form
words that relate to the title of the puzzle.

DAYS OF JOY AND AWE

1. HORS ANHAHAS   _ _ _ _   _ _ _ _ _ _ _

2. VAPORESS   _ _ _ _ _ _ _ _

3. AUNACKH   _ _ _ _ _ _ _

4. OMY PIRKUP   _ _ _   _ _ _ _ _ _

5. MINEISH REZTATE   _ _ _ _ _ _ _   _ _ _ _ _ _ _

6. OUTVASH   _ _ _ _ _ _ _

7. MATCHIS OATHR   _ _ _ _ _ _ _   _ _ _ _ _

8. OKTUSK   _ _ _ _ _ _

9. GAL B'ROME   _ _ _ _   _ _ _ _ _

10. RIPUM   _ _ _ _ _

11. UT VASEHB'T   _ _   _ _ _ _ _ _ _

12. ATHIS AVB'   _ _ _ _ _ _   _ _ _

13. ROU DISHAYOL   _ _ _ _   _ _ _ _ _ _ _

For solution see page 91

Word Search

Search the puzzle for the words listed alongside it. As you find each word, circle it or draw a line through it. The words may be spelled forward or backward and may appear horizontally, vertically, diagonally, or even around the outer corners of the puzzle.

JERUSALEM
GOLDEN CITY

S	K	E	T	A	G	S	U	C	S	A	M	A	D	C
U	C	C	M	T	H	E	R	Z	L	I	Z	X	H	S
M	O	H	I	E	L	F	N	U	R	T	B	A	E	S
T	R	A	K	N	E	S	S	E	T	M	G	V	H	W
L	E	S	V	F	G	L	H	E	O	A	I	T	O	E
A	H	S	A	I	M	S	L	T	L	L	R	D	T	S
T	T	I	O	N	A	A	S	L	O	E	R	A	C	T
I	F	D	T	E	Q	D	W	F	I	A	G	H	M	E
P	O	I	M	S	I	I	O	M	C	S	T	U	K	R
S	E	M	A	V	N	T	E	L	N	H	S	A	O	N
O	M	G	A	D	N	L	Z	O	O	E	N	K	L	W
H	O	D	O	U	S	W	I	N	U	R	T	U	L	A
H	D	W	O	R	K	L	J	M	G	F	O	O	E	L
A	S	M	O	U	N	T	S	C	O	P	U	S	K	L
S	S	A	D	A	H	M	E	H	S	A	V	D	A	Y

CARDO
CHAGALL WINDOWS
CHASSIDIM
DAMASCUS GATE
DAVID'S TOMB
DOME OF THE ROCK
EL AQSA
HADASSAH HOSPITAL
KNESSET
KOLLEK
LIONS' GATE
MIKVAOT
MOUNT OF OLIVES
MOUNT SCOPUS
MT HERZL
MUSEUMS
SHTREIMELS
SOUK
VIA DOLOROSA
WESTERN WALL
YAD VASHEM
ZOO

42

For solution see page 91

Acrostic

Find the appropriate answer to the clues listed and write the word in the numbered spaces to the right. Then transfer each letter to the corresponding numbered box in the diagram above. When done correctly, one or more sentences relating to the subject of the puzzle will be formed.

ABRAHAM

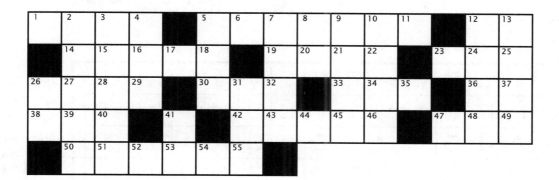

1. Sweet _____
2. Disgrace
3. Trophy, prize
4. Small city
5. _____ tub, _____ room
6. _____ man of Oz
7. Sign of boredom
8. Custom
9. Book of maps
10. Idea
11. Draw off liquid
12. Fly

1. ___ ___ ___ ___ ___
   18 23 38 7 52

2. ___ ___ ___ ___ ___
   36 22 2 11 48

3. ___ ___ ___ ___ ___
   25 30 8 16 46

4. ___ ___ ___ ___
   37 13 49 29

5. ___ ___ ___ ___
   42 51 26 9

6. ___ ___ ___
   40 20 33

7. ___ ___ ___ ___
   32 10 19 45

8. ___ ___ ___ ___ ___
   31 41 6 53 21

9. ___ ___ ___ ___ ___
   15 35 24 44 1

10. ___ ___ ___ ___ ___ ___
    47 28 12 3 54 50

11. ___ ___ ___ ___ ___
    4 39 17 27 55

12. ___ ___ ___ ___
    14 34 5 43

For solution see page 92

Word Search

Search the puzzle for the words listed alongside it. As you find each word, circle it or draw a line through it. The words may be spelled forward or backward and may appear horizontally, vertically, diagonally, or even around the outer corners of the puzzle.

LAND OF ISRAEL

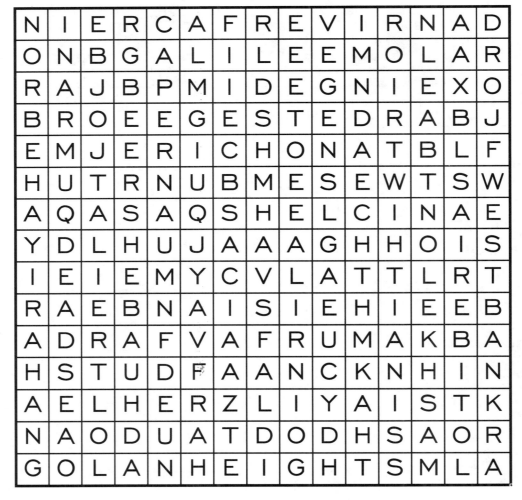

N	I	E	R	C	A	F	R	E	V	I	R	N	A	D
O	N	B	G	A	L	I	L	E	E	M	O	L	A	R
R	A	J	B	P	M	I	D	E	G	N	I	E	X	O
B	R	O	E	E	G	E	S	T	E	D	R	A	B	J
E	M	J	E	R	I	C	H	O	N	A	T	B	L	F
H	U	T	R	N	U	B	M	E	S	E	W	T	S	W
A	Q	A	S	A	Q	S	H	E	L	C	I	N	A	E
Y	D	L	H	U	J	A	A	A	G	H	H	O	I	S
I	E	I	E	M	Y	C	V	L	A	T	T	L	R	T
R	A	E	B	N	A	I	S	I	E	H	I	E	E	B
A	D	R	A	F	V	A	F	R	U	M	A	K	B	A
H	S	T	U	D	F	A	A	N	C	K	N	H	I	N
A	E	L	H	E	R	Z	L	I	Y	A	I	S	T	K
N	A	O	D	U	A	T	D	O	D	H	S	A	O	R
G	O	L	A	N	H	E	I	G	H	T	S	M	L	A

ACRE
AFULA
ASHDOD
ASHKELON
BEERSHEBA
BETHLEHEM
CAESAREA
CAPERNAUM
DEAD SEA
EILAT
EIN GEDI
GALILEE
GOLAN HEIGHTS
HAIFA
HEBRON
HERZLIYA
JERICHO
JERUSALEM
JORDAN RIVER
NAHARIYA
NAZARETH
NEGEV
NETANYA
QUMRAN
SAFED
SINAI
TEL AVIV
TIBERIAS
WEST BANK

44

For solution see page 92

Acrostic

Find the appropriate answer to the clues listed and write the word in the numbered spaces to the right. Then transfer each letter to the corresponding numbered box in the diagram above. When done correctly, one or more sentences relating to the subject of the puzzle will be formed.

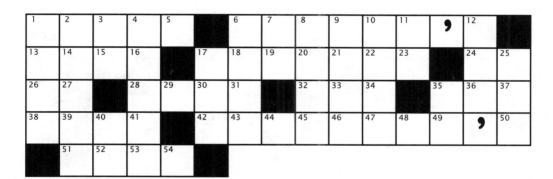

Joseph's Coat

1	2	3	4	5	■	6	7	8	9	10	11	,	12	■
13	14	15	16	■	17	18	19	20	21	22	23	■	24	25
26	27	■	28	29	30	31	■	32	33	34	■	35	36	37
38	39	40	41	■	42	43	44	45	46	47	48	49	,	50
■	51	52	53	54	■									

1. Finger ornament
2. Try for a basket
3. Court official
4. Flower holder
5. Scamp
6. Tinkerbell
7. Gelt
8. Snapshot
9. Not first
10. Elegance
11. Rock

1. ___ ___ ___ ___
   21 39 4 46

2. ___ ___ ___ ___ ___
   50 11 20 2 30

3. ___ ___ ___ ___ ___
   6 33 42 28 54

4. ___ ___ ___ ___
   51 14 44 9

5. ___ ___ ___ ___ ___
   49 18 5 3 22

6. ___ ___ ___ ___ ___
   35 26 45 34 1

7. ___ ___ ___ ___ ___
   13 25 47 43 16

8. ___ ___ ___ ___ ___
   10 38 32 27 52

9. ___ ___ ___ ___ ___ ___
   8 48 24 40 15 23

10. ___ ___ ___ ___ ___
   17 19 36 37 12

11. ___ ___ ___ ___ ___
   31 53 7 41 29

For solution see page 93

Bible Quote

Fill in the blank spaces with the letters below. The filled-in letters
will form a Bible quotation.

SYMBOL OF PEACE

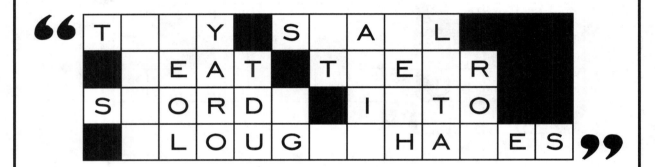

I H E H H L B

H R P N W S S

46

For solution see page 93

Fill in the blank spaces from left to right using the clues provided.

Delicious Dishes

1. Tasty carrot dish
2. Jewish dumplings (2 words)
3. Fishy appetizer
4. Stuffed crêpes
5. Jewish penicillin (2 words)
6. Potato pancakes
7. Sabbath bread
8. Sweet treat (2 words)
9. Pudding
10. Pâté (2 words)
11. Beet soup
12. Potato or kasha _____
13. Popular doughy circles
14. Jewish wontons

STRICTLY

KOSHER

For solution see page 94

Bible Stories

Fill in the blank spaces with the correct letters, then read the filled-in
letters from top to bottom to discover an appropriate title for this puzzle.

__ OLOMON

S __ PERIOR

ERE __ TED

__ OLY

__ RK

KNO __ LEDGE

BU __ LT

FIR __ T

TEMPL __

__ EEN

R __ DDLES

DISCER __ ING

JUD __ MENT

For solution see page 94

Acrostic

Find the appropriate answer to the clues listed and write the word in the numbered spaces to the right. Then transfer each letter to the corresponding numbered box in the diagram above. When done correctly, one or more sentences relating to the subject of the puzzle will be formed.

1	2	3		4	5	6		7	8	9	10		11	12
13		14	15	16	17		18	19	20	21	22		23	24
	25	26	27		28	29	30	?			31	32	33	34
35	36	37		38	39	40	41		42	43	44		45	46
47	48	49	50	51		52	53		54	55	56		57	58
59	60													

1. Writing material for blackboards
2. Gets a light sunburn
3. Grain
4. Papa; father
5. "The _____ of Music"
6. Playthings
7. To toss a baseball
8. Cookie makers
9. Land of milk and _____
10. Severe diet: bread and _____
11. Turning point; joint
12. Pay attention; see

1. ___ ___ ___ ___ ___
   59 8 40 15 30

2. ___ ___ ___ ___
   13 28 50 22

3. ___ ___ ___ ___ ___
   42 2 37 19 47

4. ___ ___ ___ ___ ___
   6 34 57 21 3

5. ___ ___ ___ ___ ___
   45 12 35 24 4

6. ___ ___ ___ ___
   48 23 10 44

7. ___ ___ ___ ___ ___
   14 49 54 33 26

8. ___ ___ ___ ___ ___ ___
   31 43 60 56 20 36

9. ___ ___ ___ ___ ___
   55 39 11 58 17

10. ___ ___ ___ ___ ___
    1 16 25 9 29

11. ___ ___ ___ ___ ___
    41 5 53 51 27

12. ___ ___ ___ ___ ___ ___
    38 52 7 46 18 32

For solution see page 95

49

Scrambled Words

Rearrange the letters below and fill in the blanks to form
words that relate to the title of the puzzle.

Peaceful Day

1. ALDAVHA   _ _ _ _ _ _ _

2. CLEANDS   _ _ _ _ _ _ _

3. EPICSOBX   _ _ _ _ _ _ _ _

4. LACHLA   _ _ _ _ _ _

5. GONE BATHSAB   _ _ _ _ _   _ _ _ _ _ _ _

6. MARYLUKE   _ _ _ _ _ _ _ _

7. ENWI   _ _ _ _

8. SNOREM   _ _ _ _ _ _

9. SKIDHUD   _ _ _ _ _ _ _

10. LITTA   _ _ _ _ _

11. FIRMAT   _ _ _ _ _ _

12. CHALE IDDO   _ _ _ _ _   _ _ _ _

13. YAD FO STER   _ _ _   _ _   _ _ _ _

For solution see page 95

Acrostic

Find the appropriate answer to the clues listed and write the word in the numbered spaces to the right. Then transfer each letter to the corresponding numbered box in the diagram above. When done correctly, one or more sentences relating to the subject of the puzzle will be formed.

Solomon

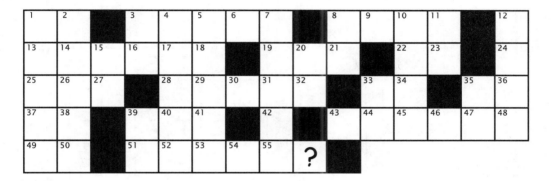

1. Dismal

2. Seep

3. Call on, go to

4. Deep cut

5. Green gemstone

6. Kiddush beverage

7. Form

8. Penalty

9. Value

10. Under age, unimportant

11. Arouse

12. Take hold

1. ___ ___ ___ ___ ___ ___
   30   14   23   13   28   50

2. ___ ___ ___ ___
   40   15   54   38

3. ___ ___ ___ ___ ___
   37   25   21   1   7

4. ___ ___ ___ ___
   11   47   22   33

5. ___ ___ ___ ___
   43   36   49   5

6. ___ ___ ___ ___
   19   53   10   34

7. ___ ___ ___ ___ ___
   12   31   42   51   55

8. ___ ___ ___ ___
   2   29   18   44

9. ___ ___ ___ ___ ___
   24   17   4   32   35

10. ___ ___ ___ ___ ___
   16   9   41   45   52

11. ___ ___ ___ ___
   39   6   8   27

12. ___ ___ ___ ___ ___
   3   48   20   26   46

For solution see page 96

Word Search

Search the puzzle for the words listed alongside it. As you find each word,
circle it or draw a line through it. The words may be spelled forward or
backward and may appear horizontally, vertically, diagonally, or even around
the outer corners of the puzzle.

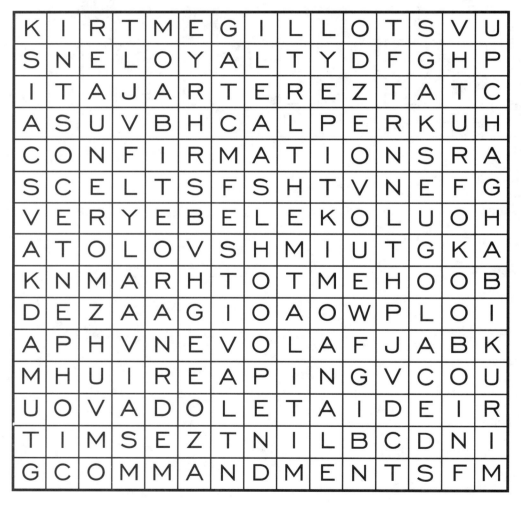

FESTIVAL OF FIRST FRUITS

K	I	R	T	M	E	G	I	L	L	O	T	S	V	U
S	N	E	L	O	Y	A	L	T	Y	D	F	G	H	P
I	T	A	J	A	R	T	E	R	E	Z	T	A	T	C
A	S	U	V	B	H	C	A	L	P	E	R	K	U	H
C	O	N	F	I	R	M	A	T	I	O	N	S	R	A
S	C	E	L	T	S	F	S	H	T	V	N	E	F	G
V	E	R	Y	E	B	E	L	E	K	O	L	U	O	H
A	T	O	L	O	V	S	H	M	I	U	T	G	K	A
K	N	M	A	R	H	T	O	T	M	E	H	O	O	B
D	E	Z	A	A	G	I	O	A	O	W	P	L	O	I
A	P	H	V	N	E	V	O	L	A	F	J	A	B	K
M	H	U	I	R	E	A	P	I	N	G	V	C	O	U
U	O	V	A	D	O	L	E	T	A	I	D	E	I	R
T	I	M	S	E	Z	T	N	I	L	B	C	D	N	I
G	C	O	M	M	A	N	D	M	E	N	T	S	F	M

AKDAMUT
ATZERET
BLINTZES
BOAZ
BOOK OF RUTH
CHAG HABIKURIM
COMMANDMENTS
CONFIRMATION
DECALOGUE
DEVOTION
FESTIVAL
GIVING THE TORAH
HARVEST
KREPLACH
LOVE
LOYALTY
MEGILLOT
MOABITE
NAOMI
PENTECOST
REAPING
SHAVUOT
SIVAN

52

For solution see page 96

Fill in the blank spaces from left to right using the clues provided.

Celebrating Passover

1. Kiddush beverage
2. Hidden dessert
3. Roasted part of lower limb
4. Sweet and nutty
5. Famous prophet
6. It's unleavened
7. Special dinner
8. Green herb
9. Once we were _____
10. Horrible outbreaks, calamities
11. Special Passover book
12. Half animal, half vegetable
13. Traditional part of table centerpiece
    (2 words)

N
O

B
R
E
A
D

P
L
E
A
S
E

Scrambled Words

Rearrange the letters below and fill in the blanks to form
words that relate to the title of the puzzle.

HARVEST TIME

1. ORGET   _ _ _ _ _

2. VALLU   _ _ _ _ _

3. KUKTOS   _ _ _ _ _ _

4. SKOREB   _ _ _ _ _ _

5. ISHIRT   _ _ _ _ _ _

6. BSHOOT   _ _ _ _ _ _

7. VITALEFS   _ _ _ _ _ _ _ _

8. LOWWIL   _ _ _ _ _ _

9. STARBECLEAN   _ _ _ _ _ _ _ _ _ _ _

10. AHSONHA ARAB   _ _ _ _ _ _ _   _ _ _ _

11. TRYMEL   _ _ _ _ _ _

12. CROPSNOISE   _ _ _ _ _ _ _ _ _ _

13. ITCHSAM RATHO   _ _ _ _ _ _ _   _ _ _ _ _

For solution see page 97

Acrostic

Find the appropriate answer to the clues listed and write the word in the numbered spaces to the right. Then transfer each letter to the corresponding numbered box in the diagram above. When done correctly, one or more sentences relating to the subject of the puzzle will be formed.

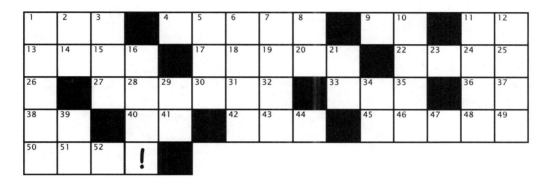

1	2	3		4	5	6	7	8		9	10		11	12
13	14	15	16		17	18	19	20	21		22	23	24	25
26		27	28	29	30	31	32		33	34	35		36	37
38	39		40	41		42	43	44		45	46	47	48	49
50	51	52	!											

1. Not loose

2. Admirers

3. Glisten; gleam

4. Where birds live

5. Small piece of land; storyline

6. Spirit

7. Impertinent; not stale

8. Upper leg

9. Declare

10. Part of skeleton

11. Hinder; postpone

1. __ __ __ __ __
   20   28   13   25   1

2. __ __ __ __
   4   33   50   19

3. __ __ __ __ __
   21   30   12   34   3

4. __ __ __ __ __
   39   47   7   31   52

5. __ __ __ __
   45   17   40   26

6. __ __ __ __ __
   24   14   43   32   8

7. __ __ __ __ __
   10   46   22   48   37

8. __ __ __ __ __
   51   2   23   29   41

9. __ __ __ __ __
   16   36   6   15   49

10. __ __ __ __
   42   9   27   38

11. __ __ __ __ __
   35   5   11   18   44

For solution see page 98

STRONGMAN SAMSON

Across:
3. False woman
6. To get even
8. Muscles
10. Evil men
11. Treachery

Down:
1. Big guy
2. Biblical Schwarzenegger
4. To gather, reap
5. Jail
7. Metal bindings
9. Sightless
10. Self-esteem

For solution see page 98

Scrambled Words

Rearrange the letters below and fill in the blanks to form
words that relate to the title of the puzzle.

Spring Festival

1. GLOTLIME   _ _ _ _ _ _ _ _

2. FROMICNATION   _ _ _ _ _ _ _ _ _ _ _ _

3. INGRAPE   _ _ _ _ _ _ _

4. TSHAVER   _ _ _ _ _ _ _

5. HURT   _ _ _ _

6. IMOAN   _ _ _ _ _

7. BOATIME   _ _ _ _ _ _ _

8. STRIF SUFITR   _ _ _ _ _ _ _ _ _ _ _ _

9. VOTENIOD   _ _ _ _ _ _ _ _

10. TOYALLY   _ _ _ _ _ _ _

11. ZABO   _ _ _ _

12. HASTUVO   _ _ _ _ _ _ _

13. GACH HASACME   _ _ _ _ _ _ _ _ _ _ _ _

Acrostic

Find the appropriate answer to the clues listed and write the word in the numbered spaces to the right. Then transfer each letter to the corresponding numbered box in the diagram above. When done correctly, one or more sentences relating to the subject of the puzzle will be formed.

Garden of Eden

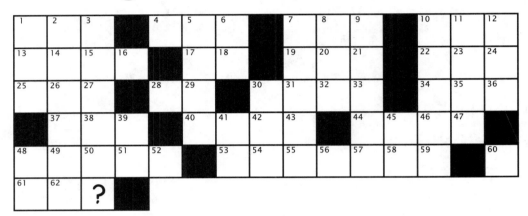

1. Broad
1. ___ ___ ___ ___
   10 54 36 26

2. Express gratitude
2. ___ ___ ___ ___ ___
   52 2   23 18 44

3. Challenge
3. ___ ___ ___ ___
   4   48 55 30

4. Son of Jacob
4. ___ ___ ___
   39 56 35

5. Exceeded
5. ___ ___ ___ ___ ___ ___
   28 51 19 25 14 37

6. Intolerant person
6. ___ ___ ___ ___ ___
   49 17 22 46 7

7. Adult females
7. ___ ___ ___ ___ ___
   1   50 53 12 33

8. Excavate
8. ___ ___ ___ ___ ___ ___
   13 61 9   31 60 42

9. Buckeye state
9. ___ ___ ___ ___
   62 20 38 3

10. Pay attention
10. ___ ___ ___ ___
    41 32 21 6

11. Bewitch
11. ___ ___ ___ ___ ___ ___ ___
    59 27 57 8   34 15 40

12. Advertising circular
12. ___ ___ ___ ___ ___
    29 58 43 11 24

13. Feathered appendage
13. ___ ___ ___ ___
    47 5   45 16

For solution see page 99

Crossword

Fill in the blank spaces from left to right using the clues provided.

The Fretting Prophet

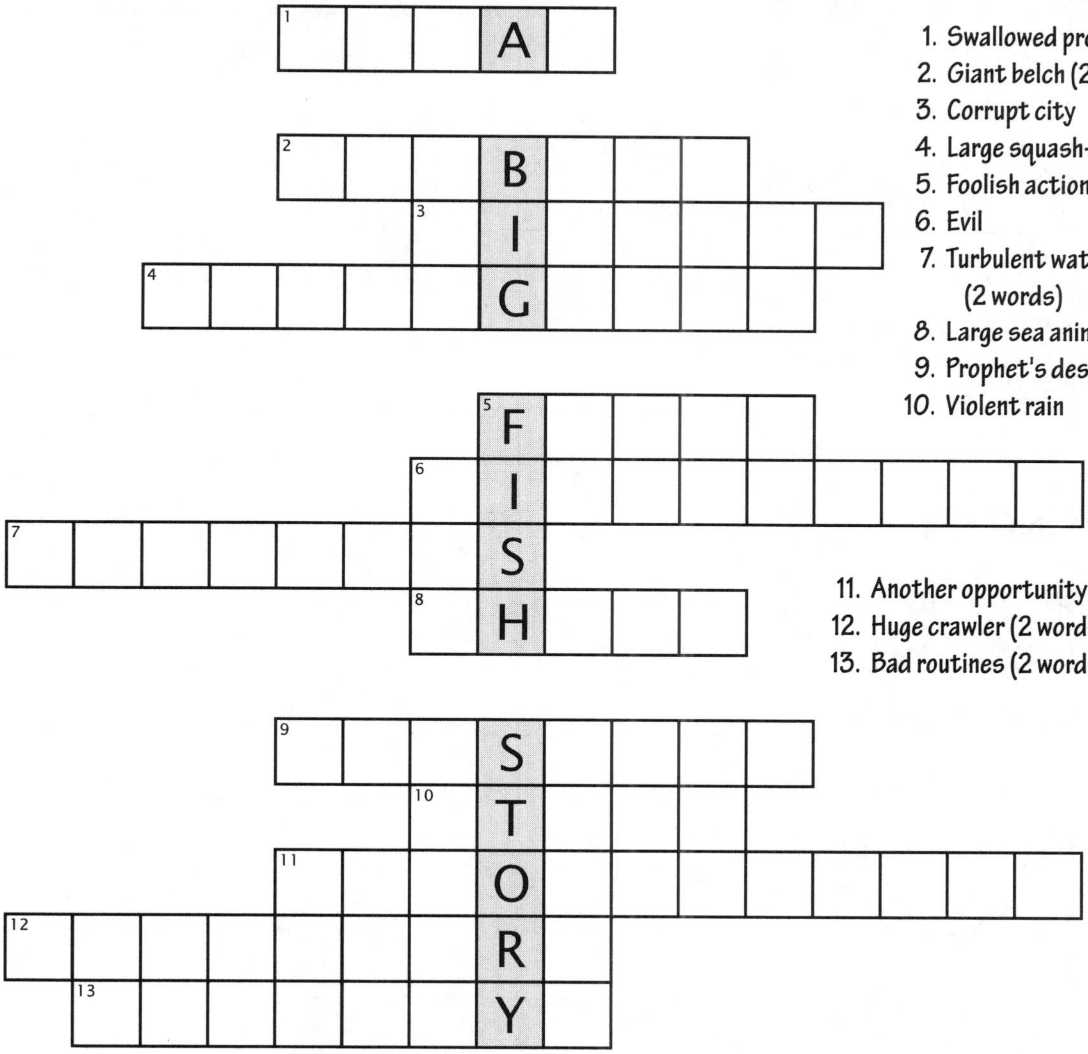

A
BIG
FISH
STORY

1. Swallowed prophet
2. Giant belch (2 words)
3. Corrupt city
4. Large squash- like plant
5. Foolish action
6. Evil
7. Turbulent waters (2 words)
8. Large sea animal
9. Prophet's destination
10. Violent rain
11. Another opportunity (2 words)
12. Huge crawler (2 words)
13. Bad routines (2 words)

For solution see page 100

Scrambled Words

Rearrange the letters below and fill in the blanks to form
words that relate to the title of the puzzle.

DAY OF PENITENCE

1. LOK DINER   __ __ __ __ __ __ __ __

2. LA THEC   __ __ __ __ __ __

3. ALIEN   __ __ __ __ __

4. RACYHIT   __ __ __ __ __ __ __

5. OKRIZY   __ __ __ __ __ __

6. SINGAFT   __ __ __ __ __ __ __

7. UNMASHA   __ __ __ __ __ __ __

8. HIDSKAD   __ __ __ __ __ __ __

9. TEAMNOTEN   __ __ __ __ __ __ __ __ __

10. GRIMNOUN   __ __ __ __ __ __ __ __

11. NNPRTCAEEE   __ __ __ __ __ __ __ __ __ __

12. SCONEIFSNO   __ __ __ __ __ __ __ __ __ __

13. OMY KRIPUP   __ __ __ __ __ __ __ __ __ __

For solution see page 100

Acrostic

Find the appropriate answer to the clues listed and write the word in the numbered spaces to the right. Then transfer each letter to the corresponding numbered box in the diagram above. When done correctly, one or more sentences relating to the subject of the puzzle will be formed.

Noah

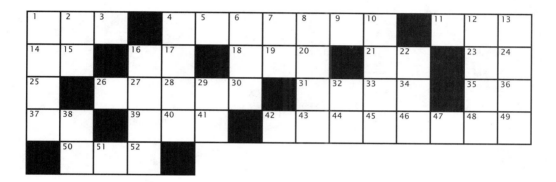

1. Prison
2. Hue
3. Four weeks
4. Secondhand
5. King of beasts
6. Froth
7. _____ constrictor
8. Israel
9. Dull pain
10. Discoloration
11. Blameworthy
12. Pull, attract

1. ___ ___ ___ ___
   35 12 47 3

2. ___ ___ ___ ___ ___
   14 51 9 36 27

3. ___ ___ ___ ___ ___
   11 39 5 23 34

4. ___ ___ ___ ___
   24 20 13 31

5. ___ ___ ___ ___
   43 16 32 48

6. ___ ___ ___ ___
   42 52 4 7

7. ___ ___ ___
   21 25 45

8. ___ ___ ___ ___
   50 6 44 38

9. ___ ___ ___ ___
   8 26 15 29

10. ___ ___ ___ ___ ___
   10 46 33 28 17

11. ___ ___ ___ ___ ___ ___
   49 40 37 2 18 22

12. ___ ___ ___ ___
   30 41 1 19

For solution see page 101

Diagram

FEAST OF LOTS

ACROSS:

1. Three-cornered pastry
2. Joyful event
3. This holiday
4. Noisemakers
5. Valuable fuel
6. Wicked man
7. Former queen
8. King
9. Special day

DOWN:

8. Hebrew month
10. Merrymaking
11. Steadfast Jew
12. Masquerade dress
13. Scroll
14. Famous Jewish queen
15. Belief

For solution see page 101

Fill in the blank spaces from left to right using the clues provided.

The First Boatbuilder

1. Biblical boat
2. } Nature's peace symbol (2 words)
3. }
4. Boatbuilder's son
5. Boatbuilder
6. Flying peace symbol
7. Biblical peak
8. Beasts
9. Multicolored arc
10. Length of time of voyage (2 words)
11. Boatbuilder's third son
12. Watery disaster
13. Snakes
14. Unkosher meat, second son
15. Feathered friends

1 A
2 L
3 A
4 S

5 N
6 O

7 U
8 M
9 B
10 R
11 E
12 L
13 L
14 A
15 S

Crossword

Fill in the blank spaces from left to right using the clues provided.

Eternal City

JERUSALEM

SIGHTS

1. Objects relating to Judaism
2. Founder's hill (2 words)
3. Revered prayer site (2 words)
4. Arab market
5. The ultra-Orthodox
6. Magnificent glasswork (2 words)

7. Sad Christian street (2 words)
8. Ultra-Orthodox area (2 words)
9. Muslim prayer center (4 words)
10. Parliament
11. Ultra-Orthodox headgear
12. Old City entrance (2 words)
13. Famous health center (2 words)
14. Noted king's burial site (2 words)
15. Heartbreaking memorial (2 words)

For solution see page 102

Word Search

Search the puzzle for the words listed alongside it. As you find each word,
circle it or draw a line through it. The words may be spelled forward or
backward and may appear horizontally, vertically, diagonally, or even around
the outer corners of the puzzle.

SHOFAR TIME

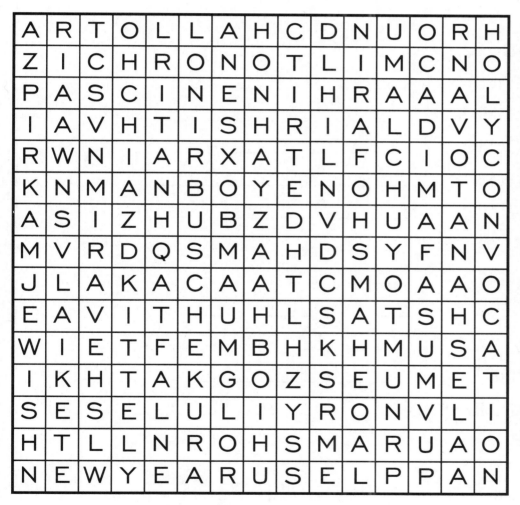

A	R	T	O	L	L	A	H	C	D	N	U	O	R	H
Z	I	C	H	R	O	N	O	T	L	I	M	C	N	O
P	A	S	C	I	N	E	N	I	H	R	A	A	A	L
I	A	V	H	T	I	S	H	R	I	A	L	D	V	Y
R	W	N	I	A	R	X	A	T	L	F	C	I	O	C
K	N	M	A	N	B	O	Y	E	N	O	H	M	T	O
A	S	I	Z	H	U	B	Z	D	V	H	U	A	A	N
M	V	R	D	Q	S	M	A	H	D	S	Y	F	N	V
J	L	A	K	A	C	A	A	T	C	M	O	A	A	O
E	A	V	I	T	H	U	H	L	S	A	T	S	H	C
W	I	E	T	F	E	M	B	H	K	H	M	U	S	A
I	K	H	T	A	K	G	O	Z	S	E	U	M	E	T
S	E	S	E	L	U	L	I	Y	R	O	N	V	L	I
H	T	L	L	N	R	O	H	S	M	A	R	U	A	O
N	E	W	Y	E	A	R	U	S	E	L	P	P	A	N

APPLES
AVINU MALKENU
ELUL
HINENI
HOLY CONVOCATION
HONEY
JEWISH NEW YEAR
KITTEL
LESHANA TOVA
MACHZOR
MALCHUYOT
MAKRI
MUSAF AMIDA
RAM'S HORN
ROSH HASHANA
ROUND CHALLOT
SHABBAT SHUVA
SHEVARIM
SHOFAR
TEKIA
TISHRI
YOM HADIN
ZICHRONOT

Scrambled Words

Rearrange the letters below and fill in the blanks to form
words that relate to the title of the puzzle.

THE TRIBES

1. HUJAD   __ __ __ __ __

2. HIREPAM   __ __ __ __ __ __ __

3. SHAMENAS   __ __ __ __ __ __ __ __

4. AIRSCASH   __ __ __ __ __ __ __ __

5. PAILTHAN   __ __ __ __ __ __ __ __

6. BLUEZUN   __ __ __ __ __ __ __

7. SHARE   __ __ __ __ __

8. AGD   __ __ __

9. BURNEE   __ __ __ __ __ __

10. AND   __ __ __

11. NOMISE   __ . __ __ __ __ __

12. JABMINNE   __ __ __ __ __ __ __ __

For solution see page 103

Crossword

Fill in the blank spaces from left to right using the clues provided.

Yom Kippur

1. Torah honors (2 words)
2. Final service
3. Religious shawl
4. Hungry time (2 words)
5. Memorial prayer
6. Doing without (2 words)
7. Nullification of vows
   (2 words)
8. Sacred scroll
9. Morality and justice
10. Mourner's prayer
11. Promises
12. Confession of sins (2 words)
13. Repentance
14. Opposite of indulgence
15. We have sinned
16. Irreligious actions

Down answer letters:
W
E
A
S
K
F
O
R
G
I
V
E
N
E
S
S

For solution see page 104

Acrostic

Find the appropriate answer to the clues listed and write the word in the numbered spaces to the right. Then transfer each letter to the corresponding numbered box in the diagram above. When done correctly, one or more sentences relating to the subject of the puzzle will be formed.

Bar Mitzvah

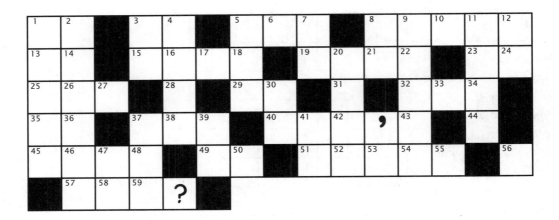

1. A, B, C, or D pill
1. __ __ __ __ __ __ __
   12 44 47 1 30 21 34

2. Rich man's ship
2. __ __ __ __ __
   4 29 57 38 15

3. Insane
3. __ __ __ __ __
   40 52 56 11 39

4. When push comes to _____
4. __ __ __ __ __
   35 14 24 45 55

5. Milk farm
5. __ __ __ __ __
   22 31 53 7 18

6. Between hips and bosom
6. __ __ __ __ __
   37 41 28 19 10

7. Water vehicle
7. __ __ __ __
   5 46 58 23

8. Mistress; lady
8. __ __ __ __ __
   32 26 51 13 3

9. Flyer
9. __ __ __ __ __ __ __
   33 54 9 20 43 49 50

10. Gelt; cash
10. __ __ __ __ __
    8 36 42 17 27

11. Fine string
11. __ __ __ __ __ __
    2 16 59 48 6 25

For solution see page 104

Crossword

Fill in the blank spaces from left to right using the clues provided.

Celebrating Rosh Hashana

1. Our Father, Our King (2 words)
2. Holiday prayerbook
3. One long blast
4. Three short musical notes
5. Unique musical instrument (2 words)
6. "Behold I Am" (holiday prayer)
7. Jewish month
8. Product of bees
9. Fruit
10. Additional prayer service
11. Holiday greeting (2 words)
12. Midnight services
13. Hebrew name for number 5 above
14. Traditional New Year breads (2 words)
15. Saturday of Repentance (2 words)

The shaded cells spell: MAKE RESOLUTIONS

For solution see page 105

Word Search

Search the puzzle for the words listed alongside it. As you find each word,
circle it or draw a line through it. The words may be spelled forward or
backward and may appear horizontally, vertically, diagonally, or even around
the outer corners of the puzzle.

YIDDISH THEATRE STARS

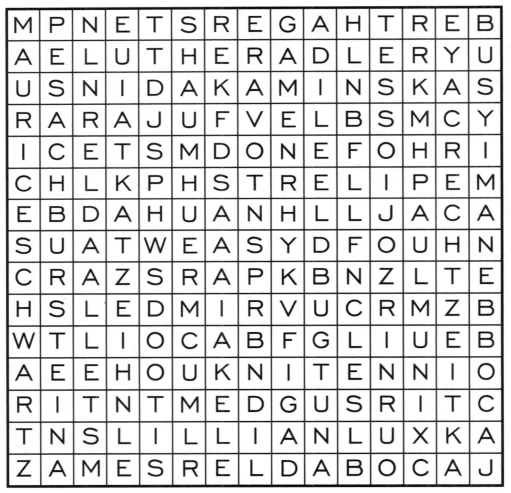

M	P	N	E	T	S	R	E	G	A	H	T	R	E	B
A	E	L	U	T	H	E	R	A	D	L	E	R	Y	U
U	S	N	I	D	A	K	A	M	I	N	S	K	A	S
R	A	R	A	J	U	F	V	E	L	B	S	M	C	Y
I	C	E	T	S	M	D	O	N	E	F	O	H	R	I
C	H	L	K	P	H	S	T	R	E	L	I	P	E	M
E	B	D	A	H	U	A	N	H	L	L	J	A	C	A
S	U	A	T	W	E	A	S	Y	D	F	O	U	H	N
C	R	A	Z	S	R	A	P	K	B	N	Z	L	T	E
H	S	L	E	D	M	I	R	V	U	C	R	M	Z	B
W	T	L	I	O	C	A	B	F	G	L	I	U	E	B
A	E	E	H	O	U	K	N	I	T	E	N	N	I	O
R	I	T	N	T	M	E	D	G	U	S	R	I	T	C
T	N	S	L	I	L	L	I	A	N	L	U	X	K	A
Z	A	M	E	S	R	E	L	D	A	B	O	C	A	J

BERNARDI
BERTHA GERSTEN
IDA KAMINSKA
JACOB ADLER
JACOB BENAMI
KATZ
LILLIAN LUX
LUTHER ADLER
MAURICE SCHWARTZ
MENASHA SKULNIK
MOLLY PICON
PAUL MUNI
PESACH BURSTEIN
RECHTZEIT
SCHILDKRAUT
STELLA ADLER
THOMASHEFSKY

70

For solution see page 105

Scrambled Words

Rearrange the letters below and fill in the blanks to form
words that relate to the title of the puzzle.

HAPPY NEW YEAR

1. UVAIN LANKEMU   _ _ _ _ _ _   _ _ _ _ _ _ _

2. HALSEAN OTAV   _ _ _ _ _ _ _ _   _ _ _ _

3. FAMUS IADMA   _ _ _ _ _ _   _ _ _ _ _

4. FAROSH   _ _ _ _ _ _

5. UNROD LATCHOL   _ _ _ _ _ _   _ _ _ _ _ _ _ _

6. RICHZOTON   _ _ _ _ _ _ _ _ _

7. NINEHI   _ _ _ _ _ _

8. HIMRAVES   _ _ _ _ _ _ _ _

9. OMY AHIND   _ _ _ _   _ _ _ _ _

10. FOROSTH   _ _ _ _ _ _ _

11. IKATE   _ _ _ _ _

12. TOUCHYALM   _ _ _ _ _ _ _ _ _

13. SHOR NAAAHHS   _ _ _ _   _ _ _ _ _ _ _

Word Search

Search the puzzle for the words listed alongside it. As you find each word,
circle it or draw a line through it. The words may be spelled forward or
backward and may appear horizontally, vertically, diagonally, or even around
the outer corners of the puzzle.

FAMOUS ZIONISTS AND ISRAELIS

```
H U L G B S U H A Y N A T E N
E S C H A P I R A M S J U D N
R L T E R S H A R O N G L X A
Z Y F S I P K L S I O O T E M
L I K S L H N E K L Z N S L Z
D O C S A F R H D S I K H N I
A N K Y N E S A A B E M A I E
I O S H P I M T A L H B P G W
V I M R S E T R L D E Q I E O
Z R A S I E P O M A S U N B L
T U U R I C K L B Y S E S R O
N G E R F M S B I A L I K U K
E N N O R D A U T N J S E T O
B E N Y E H U D A L M H R E S
H B A K T S R A Z A H S F L Y
```

ABBA EBAN
BAR ILAN
BEGIN
BEN GURION
BEN TZVI
BEN YEHUDA
BIALIK
DAYAN
ESHKOL
GOLDA MEIR
HENRIETTA SZOLD
HERZL
HESS
JABOTINSKY
KOLLEK
NETANYAHU
NORDAU
PERES
PINSKER
RABIN
SCHAPIRA
SHARON
SHAZAR
SOKOLOW
USSISHKIN
WEIZMANN

For solution see page 106

Crossword

Fill in the blank spaces from left to right using the clues provided.

Sabbath Peace

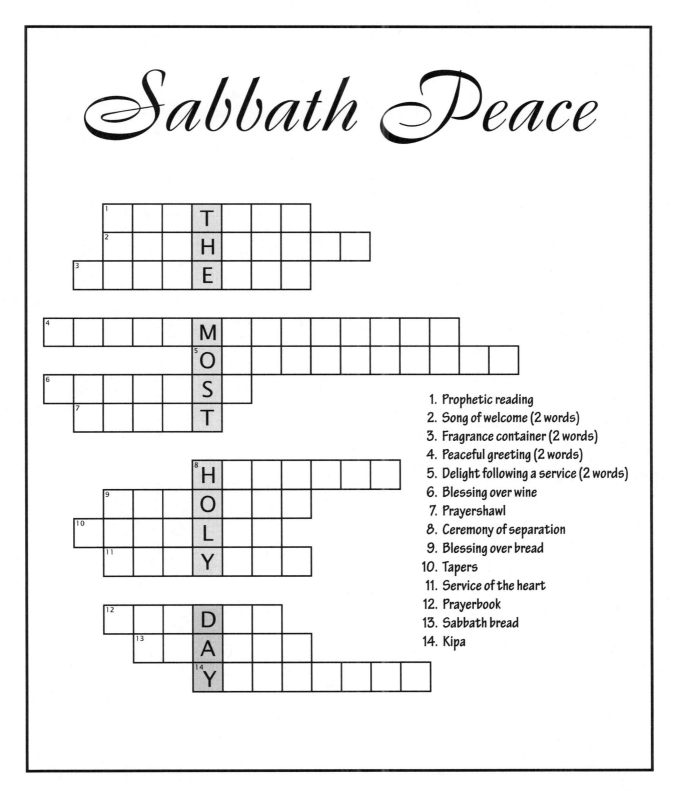

1. Prophetic reading
2. Song of welcome (2 words)
3. Fragrance container (2 words)
4. Peaceful greeting (2 words)
5. Delight following a service (2 words)
6. Blessing over wine
7. Prayershawl
8. Ceremony of separation
9. Blessing over bread
10. Tapers
11. Service of the heart
12. Prayerbook
13. Sabbath bread
14. Kipa

For solution see page 107

PUZZLE
SOLUTIONS

Solution to puzzle on page 11

THE GOLDEN RULE

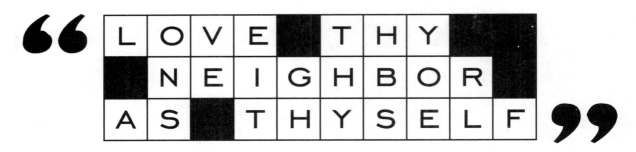

— Leviticus 19:18

Solution to puzzle on page 12

THE BROTHERS

I see that Cain and Abel were sons of Adam and Eve, but when Cain slew Abel his excuse was "Am I my brother's keeper?"

Solution to puzzle on page 13

FAITH IN GOD

T	H	E			L	O	R	D	
	I	S			M	Y			
S	H	E	P	H	E	R	D		
		I			S	H	A	L	L
N	O	T			W	A	N	T	

— Psalm 23:1

Solution to puzzle on page 14

Afikomon

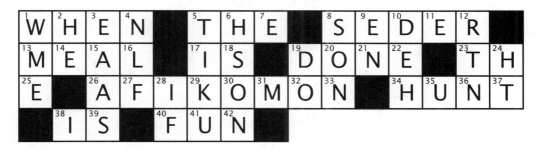

1. D R I N K
   10 12 38 33 29
2. M I N E
   31 17 36 9
3. S H U N
   39 6 35 21
4. W H I T E
   1 34 28 23 14
5. F U N D
   27 41 42 19

6. H O T E L
   24 20 37 3 16
7. F A M E
   40 26 13 7
8. N O S E
   4 32 8 22
9. S H O E
   18 2 30 11
10. E A T
   25 15 5

Solution to puzzle on page 15

ANCIENT ENEMY

Antiochus was the name of the Greek King who ruled over Syria & Palestine in the days of the Maccabees.

Solution to puzzle on page 16

A TEMPLE MIRACLE

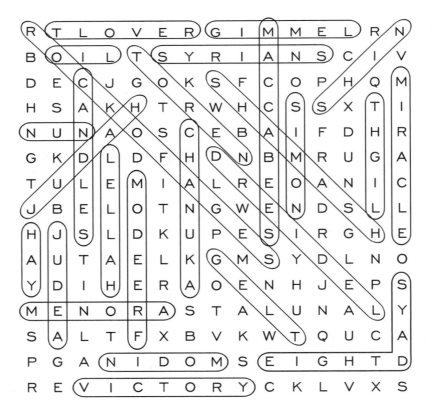

Solution to puzzle on page 17

EV **E**
SERPE **N** T
A **D** AM

DIS **O** BEYED
F IG LEAF

EX **P** ELLED
CRE **A** TION
WA **R** NING
G **A** RDEN
FORBI **D** DEN
FRU **I** T
CA **S** T OUT
ED **E** N

Solution to puzzle on page 18

CAIN'S QUESTION

A	M		I		M	Y	
B	R	O	T	H	E	R	'S
K	E	E	P	E	R	?	

— Genesis 4:9

Solution to puzzle on page 19

Daniel

¹B	²R	³A	⁴V	⁵E		⁶D	⁷A	⁸N	⁹I	¹⁰E	¹¹L		¹²I	¹³N
	¹⁴T	¹⁵H	¹⁶E		¹⁷L	¹⁸I	¹⁹O	²⁰N	²¹'S		²²D	²³E	²⁴N
	²⁵T	²⁶R	²⁷U	²⁸L	²⁹Y		³⁰A		³¹H	³²E	³³R	³⁴O	
³⁵T	³⁶O		³⁷A	³⁸L	³⁹L		⁴⁰M	⁴¹E	⁴²N	

1. $\underset{37}{A}\ \underset{11}{L}\ \underset{12}{I}\ \underset{5}{E}\ \underset{20}{N}$

2. $\underset{1}{B}\ \underset{38}{L}\ \underset{19}{O}\ \underset{8}{N}\ \underset{22}{D}\ \underset{16}{E}$

3. $\underset{31}{H}\ \underset{32}{E}\ \underset{30}{A}\ \underset{4}{V}\ \underset{10}{E}\ \underset{13}{N}$

4. $\underset{26}{R}\ \underset{34}{O}\ \underset{14}{T}\ \underset{3}{A}\ \underset{35}{T}\ \underset{23}{E}$

5. $\underset{25}{T}\ \underset{15}{H}\ \underset{33}{R}\ \underset{36}{O}\ \underset{24}{N}\ \underset{41}{E}$

6. $\underset{6}{D}\ \underset{27}{U}\ \underset{17}{L}\ \underset{39}{L}$

7. $\underset{2}{R}\ \underset{7}{A}\ \underset{18}{I}\ \underset{42}{N}\ \underset{29}{Y}$

8. $\underset{21}{S}\ \underset{28}{L}\ \underset{9}{I}\ \underset{40}{M}$

Solution to puzzle on page 20

ESCAPE FROM SLAVERY

1. EGYPT
2. MATZA
3. EXODUS
4. SEDER
5. AFIKOMON
6. CHAMETZ
7. CHAD GADYA
8. CHAROSET
9. ISRAELITES
10. HAGGADA
11. ELIJAH
12. BITTER HERBS
13. PASSOVER

JONAH

¹W	²E		³H	⁴A	⁵I	⁶L		⁷T	⁸H	⁹I	¹⁰S		¹¹H	¹²E
¹³R	¹⁴O		¹⁵I	¹⁶N		¹⁷A	¹⁸L	¹⁹L		²⁰H	²¹I	²²S		²³G
²⁴L	²⁵O	²⁶R	²⁷Y		²⁸F	²⁹O	³⁰R		³¹J	³²O	³³N	³⁴A	³⁵H
³⁶H	³⁷A	³⁸D		³⁹A		⁴⁰W	⁴¹H	⁴²A	⁴³L	⁴⁴E		⁴⁵O	⁴⁶F
⁴⁷A		⁴⁸S	⁴⁹T	⁵⁰O	⁵¹R	⁵²Y							

1. H E L L O
   8 2 43 18 50

2. S H A R E
   48 35 39 51 12

3. G R A I N
   23 30 37 5 16

4. H A S H
   36 42 22 20

5. F L A W
   46 24 17 40

6. H I S T O R Y
   3 21 10 49 29 13 27

7. J O L L Y
   31 14 19 6 52

8. H A W A I I
   41 34 1 47 15 9

9. D A R N
   38 4 26 33

10. F O O T
    28 45 25 7

11. H O E
    11 32 44

HEARTBURN

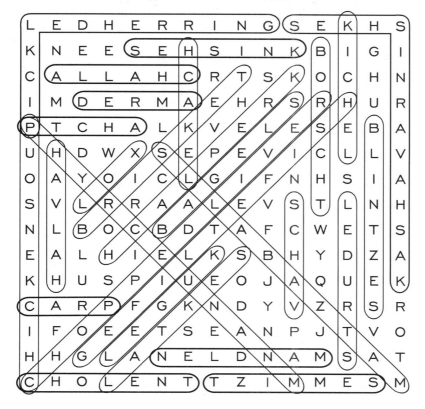

L	E	D	H	E	R	R	I	N	G	S	E	K	H	S
K	N	E	E	S	E	H	S	I	N	K	B	I	G	I
C	A	L	L	A	H	C	R	T	S	K	O	C	H	N
I	M	D	E	R	M	A	E	H	R	S	R	H	U	R
P	T	C	H	A	L	K	V	E	L	E	S	E	B	A
U	H	D	W	X	S	E	P	E	V	I	C	L	L	V
O	A	Y	O	I	C	L	G	I	F	N	H	S	I	A
S	V	L	R	R	A	A	L	E	V	S	T	L	N	H
N	L	B	O	C	B	D	T	A	F	C	W	E	T	S
E	A	L	H	I	E	L	K	S	B	H	Y	D	Z	A
K	H	U	S	P	I	U	E	O	J	A	Q	U	E	K
C	A	R	P	F	G	K	N	D	Y	V	Z	R	S	R
I	F	O	E	E	T	S	E	A	N	P	J	T	V	O
H	H	G	L	A	N	E	L	D	N	A	M	S	A	T
C	H	O	L	E	N	T	Z	I	M	M	E	S	M

(81)

Solution to puzzle on page 23

Cain

¹W	²H	³Y		⁴W	⁵A	⁶S	⁷N	’	⁸T		⁹C	¹⁰A	¹¹I	¹²N
	¹³L	¹⁴I	¹⁵K	¹⁶E		¹⁷H	¹⁸I	¹⁹S		²⁰B	²¹R	²²O	²³T	²⁴H
²⁵E	²⁶R	?		²⁷B	²⁸E	²⁹C	³⁰A	³¹U	³²S	³³E		³⁴H	³⁵E	
³⁶W	³⁷A	³⁸S		³⁹N	⁴⁰O	⁴¹T		⁴²A	⁴³S		⁴⁴A	⁴⁵B	⁴⁶L	⁴⁷E
	⁴⁸A	⁴⁹S		⁵⁰A	⁵¹B	⁵²E	⁵³L							

1. $\underset{6}{S}\ \underset{24}{H}\ \underset{44}{A}\ \underset{15}{K}\ \underset{28}{E}$

2. $\underset{20}{B}\ \underset{13}{L}\ \underset{47}{E}\ \underset{50}{A}\ \underset{8}{T}$

3. $\underset{4}{W}\ \underset{30}{A}\ \underset{43}{S}\ \underset{2}{H}$

4. $\underset{27}{B}\ \underset{21}{R}\ \underset{40}{O}\ \underset{36}{W}\ \underset{39}{N}$

5. $\underset{26}{R}\ \underset{10}{A}\ \underset{14}{I}\ \underset{38}{S}\ \underset{33}{E}$

6. $\underset{32}{S}\ \underset{1}{W}\ \underset{48}{A}\ \underset{3}{Y}$

7. $\underset{34}{H}\ \underset{22}{O}\ \underset{31}{U}\ \underset{19}{S}\ \underset{52}{E}$

8. $\underset{9}{C}\ \underset{42}{A}\ \underset{45}{B}\ \underset{18}{I}\ \underset{12}{N}$

9. $\underset{49}{S}\ \underset{53}{L}\ \underset{16}{E}\ \underset{35}{E}\ \underset{23}{T}$

10. $\underset{29}{C}\ \underset{46}{L}\ \underset{25}{E}\ \underset{37}{A}\ \underset{7}{N}$

11. $\underset{17}{H}\ \underset{5}{A}\ \underset{51}{B}\ \underset{11}{I}\ \underset{41}{T}$

Solution to puzzle on page 24

MARDI GRAS

1. MORDECAI
2. ESTHER
3. GALLOWS
4. CARNIVAL
5. VASHTI
6. GROGGERS
7. AHASUEROS
8. HAMAN
9. COSTUMES
10. PERSIA
11. HAMANTASHEN
12. PURIM
13. NOISE

Solution to puzzle on page 25

A RESTFUL DAY

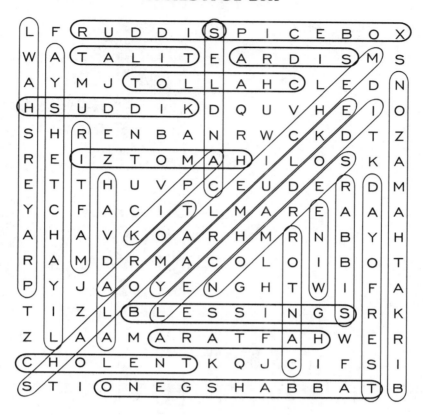

Solution to puzzle on page 26

Purim

¹T	²H	³E		⁴P	⁵U	⁶R	⁷I	⁸M		⁹C	¹⁰A	¹¹R	¹²N	¹³I
¹⁴V	¹⁵A	¹⁶L		¹⁷H	¹⁸A	¹⁹S		²⁰Z	²¹E	²²S	²³T		²⁴B	²⁵U
²⁶T		²⁷W	²⁸H	²⁹A	³⁰T		³¹I		³²L	³³I	³⁴K	³⁵E		³⁶B
³⁷E	³⁸S	³⁹T		⁴⁰I	⁴¹S		⁴²N	⁴³O	⁴⁴S	⁴⁵H	⁴⁶I	⁴⁷N	⁴⁸G	
⁴⁹H	⁵⁰A	⁵¹M	⁵²A	⁵³N	⁵⁴T	⁵⁵A	⁵⁶S	⁵⁷C	⁵⁸H	⁵⁹E	⁶⁰N			

1. $\underset{60}{N}\ \underset{25}{U}\ \underset{39}{T}$

2. $\underset{22}{S}\ \underset{1}{T}\ \underset{7}{I}\ \underset{53}{N}\ \underset{48}{G}$

3. $\underset{16}{L}\ \underset{5}{U}\ \underset{47}{N}\ \underset{57}{C}\ \underset{45}{H}$

4. $\underset{15}{A}\ \underset{33}{I}\ \underset{51}{M}$

5. $\underset{4}{P}\ \underset{55}{A}\ \underset{26}{T}\ \underset{9}{C}\ \underset{58}{H}$

6. $\underset{54}{T}\ \underset{17}{H}\ \underset{40}{I}\ \underset{12}{N}$

7. $\underset{36}{B}\ \underset{52}{A}\ \underset{19}{S}\ \underset{34}{K}\ \underset{3}{E}\ \underset{30}{T}$

8. $\underset{27}{W}\ \underset{10}{A}\ \underset{56}{S}\ \underset{2}{H}\ \underset{21}{E}\ \underset{38}{S}$

9. $\underset{8}{M}\ \underset{43}{O}\ \underset{23}{T}\ \underset{49}{H}$

10. $\underset{28}{H}\ \underset{46}{I}\ \underset{14}{V}\ \underset{59}{E}\ \underset{41}{S}$

11. $\underset{24}{B}\ \underset{32}{L}\ \underset{29}{A}\ \underset{20}{Z}\ \underset{37}{E}$

12. $\underset{6}{R}\ \underset{18}{A}\ \underset{31}{I}\ \underset{44}{S}\ \underset{13}{I}\ \underset{42}{N}$

13. $\underset{35}{E}\ \underset{50}{A}\ \underset{11}{R}$

Solution to puzzle on page 27

S **T** RONG
RED CO **R** D
JOSH **U** A
AM **M** ORITES
P ROMISED LAND
J **E** RICHO
FAI **T** H

COLLA **P** SE
SHIL **O** H
HIGH **W** ALLS
TRIB **E**
DA **R** ING

Solution to puzzle on page 28

MUSCLE MAN

1.	S	H	O	V	E	L		
	10	38	46	15	42	31		

2.	G	R	A	I	N		
	24	50	47	33	6		

3.	M	E	E	T	S
	3	36	16	48	19

4. T O A S T
   37 22 26 1 44

5. H E A R T
   41 45 8 21 34

6. W O M A N
   7 5 25 51 23

7. B U S H Y
   49 30 4 13 18

8. A C T O R
   14 12 40 29 17

9. B A N D A N A
   35 43 27 32 2 52 39

10. C U T S
    28 11 20 9

Solution to puzzle on page 29

Winter Holiday

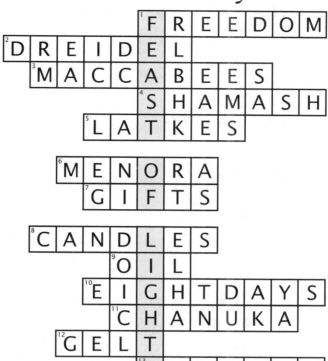

(Crossword grid, across answers):

FREEDOM
DREIDEL
MACCABEES
SHAMASH
LATKES
MENORA
GIFTS
CANDLES
OIL
EIGHTDAYS
CHANUKA
GELT
SYRIANS

Solution to puzzle on page 30

JOSHUA

¹W	²H	³E	⁴N		⁵J	⁶O	⁷S	⁸H	⁹U	¹⁰A	ʼ	¹¹S		¹²T
¹³R	¹⁴U	¹⁵M	¹⁶P	¹⁷E	¹⁸T	¹⁹S		²⁰T	²¹U	²²M	²³B	²⁴L	²⁵E	²⁶D
	²⁷J	²⁸E	²⁹R	³⁰I	³¹C	³²H	³³O	ʼ	³⁴S		³⁵W	³⁶A	³⁷L	³⁸L
³⁹S		⁴⁰W	⁴¹A	⁴²S		⁴³I	⁴⁴T		⁴⁵T	⁴⁶H	⁴⁷E		⁴⁸F	⁴⁹I
⁵⁰R	⁵¹S	⁵²T		⁵³R	⁵⁴O	⁵⁵C	⁵⁶K		⁵⁷A	⁵⁸N	⁵⁹D		⁶⁰R	⁶¹O
⁶²L	⁶³L	?												

1. S W A L L O W
   19 40 10 37 24 54 1

2. J U M P E D
   5 21 22 16 47 26

3. F I N D
   48 30 58 59

4. H E R O I C
   46 25 13 33 43 31

5. S T R O L L
   42 12 50 6 38 63

6. B L U S T E R
   23 62 14 39 52 3 60

7. S H O R T
   51 2 61 29 20

8. T H A N K
   18 8 36 4 56

9. S T R A W
   11 45 53 57 35

10. J U S T I C E E
    27 9 34 44 49 55 17

11. S H A M E
    7 32 41 15 28

85

Solution to puzzle on page 31

J OSEPH
M **A** NY
C OLORED
C **O** AT
FORCI **B** LY
EN **S** LAVED

TROU **B** LED
DR **E** AMS
S OLD TO
PO **T** IPHAR

S EVEN
GO **O** D YEARS
LEA **N** YEARS

Solution to puzzle on page 32

LIBERTY

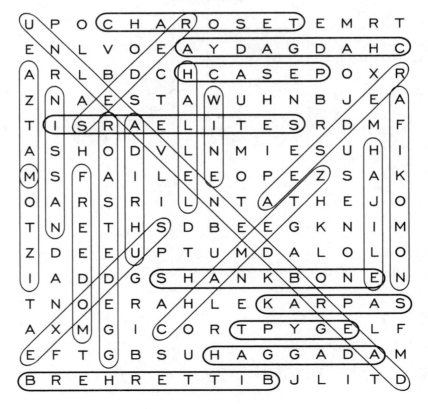

Solution to puzzle on page 33

Goliath

¹G	²O	³L	⁴I	⁵A	⁶T	⁷H		⁸S	⁹N	¹⁰E	¹¹E	¹²R	¹³E	¹⁴D
	¹⁵A	¹⁶T		¹⁷H	¹⁸I	¹⁹S		²⁰P	²¹U	²²N	²³Y		²⁴F	²⁵O
²⁶E		²⁷B	²⁸U	²⁹T		³⁰D	³¹A	³²V	³³I	³⁴D	³⁵'S			³⁶S
³⁷L	³⁸I	³⁹N	⁴⁰G	⁴¹S	⁴²H	⁴³O	⁴⁴T		⁴⁵L	⁴⁶A	⁴⁷I	⁴⁸D		⁴⁹H
⁵⁰I	⁵¹M		⁵²L	⁵³O	⁵⁴W									

1. G O A T
    40 53 15 6
2. S H A V E
    8 42 46 32 13
3. U N I T E
    28 22 33 44 10
4. F L A S H
    24 3 31 41 17
5. B O I L
    27 2 38 52
6. D U S T
    14 21 19 29
7. D R I E D
    30 12 47 26 48
8. P O N Y
    20 43 9 23
9. M A I L
    51 5 18 37
10. H I N T S
    49 4 39 16 35
11. G L I D E
    1 45 50 34 11
12. S H O W
    36 7 25 54

Solution to puzzle on page 34

Jewish Laws

¹S	T	O	N	E	T	A	B	L	E	T	S
		²C	O	V	E	N	A	N	T		
		³M	O	U	N	T	S	I	N	A	I

⁴G	O	L	D	E	N	C	A	L	F
			⁵M	O	S	E	S
⁶R	E	M	E	M	B	E	R
			⁷M	A	T	Z	A
⁸P	L	A	G	U	E	S
⁹B	U	R	N	I	N	G	B	U	S	H
	¹⁰R	E	D	S	E	A
	¹¹M	I	T	Z	V	O	T
	¹²E	X	O	D	U	S
¹³O	N	E	G	O	D
¹⁴P	R	O	P	H	E	T
	¹⁵O	B	S	E	R	V	A	N	C	E

87

Solution to puzzle on page 35

REPUTATION ABOVE ALL

" A   GOOD   NAME
I S   BETTER
THAN   GREAT
RICHES "

— Proverbs 22:1

Solution to puzzle on page 36

A QUEEN'S TRIUMPH

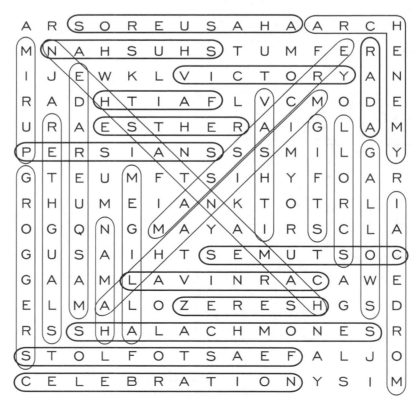

INTRE **P** ID
DANIE **L**
    L **I** ONS DEN
KIN **G** DARIUS
UN **H** ARMED
HANDWRI **T** ING

JEAL **O** USY
    F IERY

FURN **A** CE

MES **H** ACH
AB **E** D-NEGO
SHAD **R** ACH
    C **O** URAGEOUS

Bridegroom

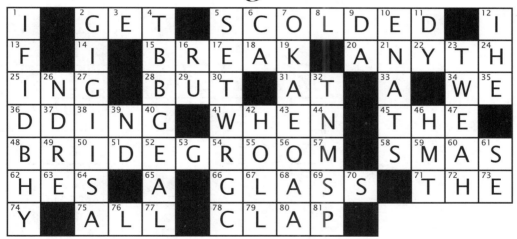

¹I		²G	³E	⁴T		⁵S	⁶C	⁷O	⁸L	⁹D	¹⁰E	¹¹D		¹²I
¹³F		¹⁴I		¹⁵B	¹⁶R	¹⁷E	¹⁸A	¹⁹K		²⁰A	²¹N	²²Y	²³T	²⁴H
²⁵I	²⁶N	²⁷G		²⁸B	²⁹U	³⁰T		³¹A	³²T		³³A		³⁴W	³⁵E
³⁶D	³⁷D	³⁸I	³⁹N	⁴⁰G		⁴¹W	⁴²H	⁴³E	⁴⁴N		⁴⁵T	⁴⁶H	⁴⁷E	
⁴⁸B	⁴⁹R	⁵⁰I	⁵¹D	⁵²E	⁵³G	⁵⁴R	⁵⁵O	⁵⁶O	⁵⁷M		⁵⁸S	⁵⁹M	⁶⁰A	⁶¹S
⁶²H	⁶³E	⁶⁴S		⁶⁵A		⁶⁶G	⁶⁷L	⁶⁸A	⁶⁹S	⁷⁰S		⁷¹T	⁷²H	⁷³E
⁷⁴Y		⁷⁵A	⁷⁶L	⁷⁷L		⁷⁸C	⁷⁹L	⁸⁰A	⁸¹P					

1. A N I M A L
   33 21 14 57 65 77

2. H O O D
   42 55 7 37

3. B A D G E S
   15 75 51 2 35 69

4. K N I T T I N G
   19 39 25 71 4 12 44 66

5. W I N D Y
   41 38 26 11 22

6. W A G E S
   34 18 53 47 5

7. H E A L T H Y
   62 10 31 67 45 24 74

8. B U R G L A R
   48 29 54 27 8 80 16

9. S M I L E
   61 59 1 79 17

10. S C R A T C H
   58 6 49 20 32 78 46

11. P I E S
   81 50 73 64

12. D E F E A T E D
   36 63 13 3 68 30 43 9

13. H O S T
   72 56 70 23

14. B A G E L
   28 60 40 52 76

Solution to puzzle on page 39

Celebrate With Lights

1. LATKES
2. ROCK OF AGES
3. MACCABEES
4. DREIDEL
5. MENORA
6. SHAMASH
7. ANTIOCHUS
8. SYRIANS
9. EIGHT DAYS
10. DEDICATION
11. PRESENTS
12. KITTEL
13. CHANUKA

Solution to puzzle on page 40

CHANUKA

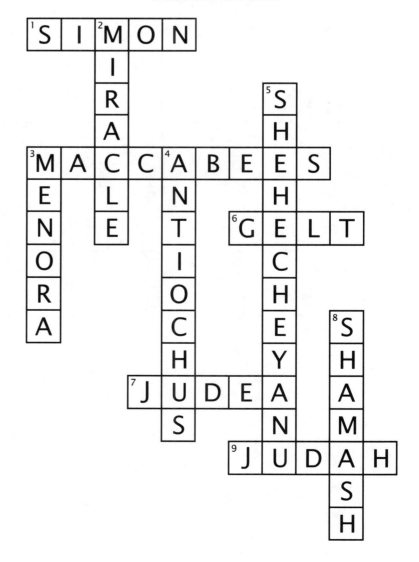

Solution to puzzle on page 41

DAYS OF JOY AND AWE

1. ROSH HASHANA
2. PASSOVER
3. CHANUKA
4. YOM KIPPUR
5. SHEMINI ATZERET
6. SHAVUOT
7. SIMCHAT TORAH
8. SUKKOT
9. LAG B'OMER
10. PURIM
11. TU B'SHEVAT
12. TISHA B'AV
13. OUR HOLIDAYS

Solution to puzzle on page 42

JERUSALEM GOLDEN CITY

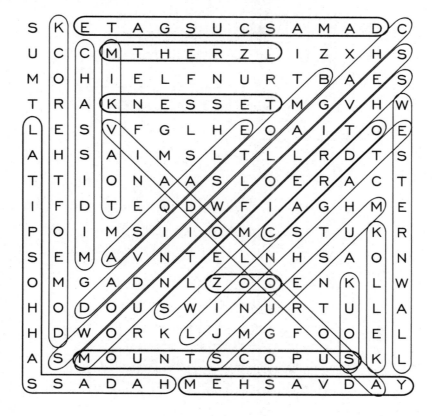

Solution to puzzle on page 43

ABRAHAM

¹S	²A	³I	D		⁵A	⁶B	⁷R	⁸A	⁹H	¹⁰A	¹¹M		¹²T	¹³O
	¹⁴S	¹⁵A	¹⁶R	¹⁷A	¹⁸H		¹⁹W	²⁰I	²¹T	²²H		²³E	²⁴L	²⁵A
²⁶T	²⁷I	²⁸O	²⁹N		³⁰W	³¹H	³²Y		³³N	³⁴O	³⁵T		³⁶S	³⁷T
³⁸A	³⁹R	⁴⁰T		⁴¹A		⁴²B	⁴³R	⁴⁴A	⁴⁵N	⁴⁶D		⁴⁷N	⁴⁸E	⁴⁹W
	⁵⁰N	⁵¹A	⁵²T	⁵³I	⁵⁴O	⁵⁵N								

SAID ABRAHAM TO SARAH WITH ELATION WHY NOT START A BRAND NEW NATION

1. H E A R T
    18 23 38 7 52

2. S H A M E
    36 22 2 11 48

3. A W A R D
    25 30 8 16 46

4. T O W N
    37 13 49 29

5. B A T H
    42 51 26 9

6. T I N
    40 20 33

7. Y A W N
    32 10 19 45

8. H A B I T
    31 41 6 53 21

9. A T L A S
    15 35 24 44 1

10. N O T I O N
    47 28 12 3 54 50

11. D R A I N
    4 39 17 27 55

12. S O A R
    14 34 5 43

Solution to puzzle on page 44

LAND OF ISRAEL

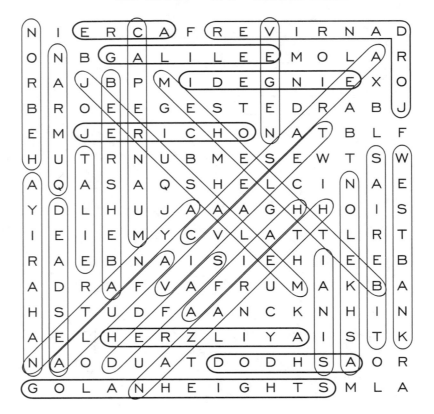

Solution to puzzle on page 45

Joseph's Coat

¹Y	²O	³U	⁴N	⁵G		⁶J	⁷O	⁸S	⁹E	¹⁰P	¹¹H	’S	¹²S	

(crossword grid)

¹Y	²O	³U	⁴N	⁵G	■	⁶J	⁷O	⁸S	⁹E	¹⁰P	¹¹H	’S	¹²■
¹³M	¹⁴A	¹⁵N	¹⁶Y	■	¹⁷C	¹⁸O	¹⁹L	²⁰O	²¹R	²²E	²³D	²⁴C	²⁵O
²⁶A	²⁷T	■	²⁸G	²⁹E	³⁰T	³¹S	■	³²O	³³U	³⁴R	■	³⁵F	³⁶A	³⁷S
³⁸H	³⁹I	⁴⁰O	⁴¹N	■	⁴²D	⁴³E	⁴⁴S	⁴⁵I	⁴⁶G	⁴⁷N	⁴⁸E	⁴⁹R	’S	⁵⁰S
■	⁵¹V	⁵²O	⁵³T	⁵⁴E	■

1. R I N G
   21 39 4 46
2. S H O O T
   50 11 20 2 30
3. J U D G E
   6 33 42 28 54
4. V A S E
   51 14 44 9
5. R O G U E
   49 18 5 3 22
6. F A I R Y
   35 26 45 34 1
7. M O N E Y
   13 25 47 43 16
8. P H O T O
   10 38 32 27 52
9. S E C O N D
   8 48 24 40 15 23
10. C L A S S
    17 19 36 37 12
11. S T O N E
    31 53 7 41 29

Solution to puzzle on page 46

SYMBOL OF PEACE

T	H	E	Y	■	S	H	A	L	L	■
■	B	E	A	T	■	T	H	E	I	R
S	W	O	R	D	S	■	I	N	T	O
■	P	L	O	U	G	H	S	H	A	R	E	S

— Ecclesiastes 2:4

Solution to puzzle on page 47

Delicious Dishes

Solution to puzzle on page 48

S OLOMON
S **U** PERIOR
ERE **C** TED
H OLY

A RK

KNO **W** LEDGE
BU **I** LT
FIR **S** T
TEMPL **E**

K EEN
r **I** DDLES
DISCER **N** ING
JUD **G** MENT

Solution to puzzle on page 49

Ark

Grid (reading across):

W H Y ■ D I D ■ T H E Y ■ N O
T ■ P L A Y ■ C A R D S ■ O N
■ T H E ■ A R K ? ■ B E C A
U S E ■ N O A H ■ W A S ■ S I
T T I N G ■ O N ■ T H E ■ D E
C K

Puzzle answer: WHY DID THEY NOT PLAY CARDS ON THE ARK? BECAUSE NOAH WAS SITTING ON THE DECK

1. C H A L K
   59 8 40 15 30
2. T A N S
   13 28 50 22
3. W H E A T
   42 2 37 19 47
4. D A D D Y
   6 34 57 21 3
5. S O U N D
   45 12 35 24 4
6. T O Y S
   48 23 10 44
7. P I T C H
   14 49 54 33 26
8. B A K E R S
   31 43 60 56 20 36
9. H O N E Y
   55 39 11 58 17
10. W A T E R
    1 16 25 9 29
11. H I N G E
    41 5 53 51 27
12. N O T I C E
    38 52 7 46 18 32

Solution to puzzle on page 50

Peaceful Day

1. HAVDALA
2. CANDLES
3. SPICEBOX
4. CHALLA
5. ONEG SHABBAT
6. YARMULKE
7. WINE
8. SERMON
9. KIDDUSH
10. TALIT
11. MAFTIR
12. LECHA DODI
13. DAY OF REST

Solution to puzzle on page 51

Solomon

¹I	²F		³G	⁴R	⁵E	⁶A	⁷T		⁸K	⁹I	¹⁰N	¹¹G		¹²S
¹³O	¹⁴L	¹⁵O	¹⁶M	¹⁷O	¹⁸N		¹⁹W	²⁰A	²¹S		²²S	²³O		²⁴W
²⁵I	²⁶S	²⁷E		²⁸M	²⁹I	³⁰G	³¹H	³²T		³³H	³⁴E		³⁵H	³⁶A
³⁷V	³⁸E		³⁹W	⁴⁰O	⁴¹N		⁴²A		⁴³J	⁴⁴E	⁴⁵O	⁴⁶P	⁴⁷A	⁴⁸R
⁴⁹D	⁵⁰Y		⁵¹P	⁵²R	⁵³I	⁵⁴Z	⁵⁵E	?						

1. G L O O M Y
   30 14 23 13 28 50
2. O O Z E
   40 15 54 38
3. V I S I T
   37 25 21 1 7
4. G A S H
   11 47 22 33
5. J A D E
   43 36 49 5
6. W I N E
   19 53 10 34

7. S H A P E
   12 31 42 51 55
8. F I N E
   2 29 18 44
9. W O R T H
   24 17 4 32 35
10. M I N O R
    16 9 41 45 52
11. W A K E
    39 6 8 27
12. G R A S P
    3 48 20 26 46

Solution to puzzle on page 52

FESTIVAL OF FIRST FRUITS

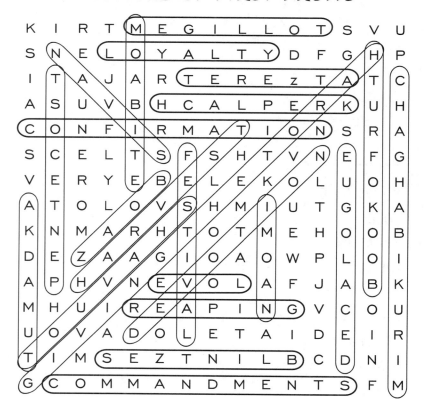

Solution to puzzle on page 53

Celebrating Passover

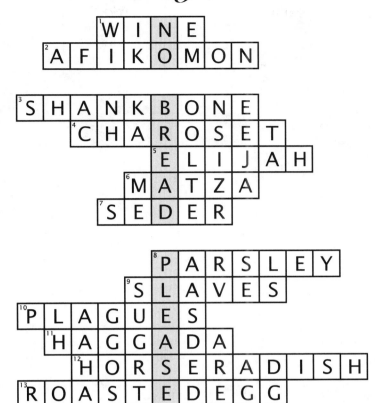

Solution to puzzle on page 54

HARVEST TIME

1. ETROG
2. LULAV
3. SUKKOT
4. BOKSER
5. TISHRI
6. BOOTHS
7. FESTIVAL
8. WILLOW
9. TABERNACLES
10. HOSHANA RABA
11. MYRTLE
12. PROCESSION
13. SIMCHAT TORAH

Solution to puzzle on page 55

Feast of Lights

¹T	²H	³E		⁴F	⁵E	⁶A	⁷S	⁸T		⁹O	¹⁰F		¹¹L	¹²I
¹³G	¹⁴H	¹⁵T	¹⁶S		¹⁷L	¹⁸A	¹⁹S	²⁰T	²¹S		²²E	²³I	²⁴G	²⁵H
²⁶T		²⁷N	²⁸I	²⁹G	³⁰H	³¹T	³²S		³³A	³⁴N	³⁵D		³⁶T	³⁷H
³⁸E	³⁹N		⁴⁰O	⁴¹H		⁴²B	⁴³O	⁴⁴Y		⁴⁵P	⁴⁶R	⁴⁷E	⁴⁸S	⁴⁹E
⁵⁰N	⁵¹T	⁵²S	!											

THE FEAST OF LIGHTS LASTS EIGHT NIGHTS AND THEN OH BOY PRESENTS!

1. T I G H T
   20 28 13 25 1
2. F A N S
   4 33 50 19
3. S H I N E
   21 30 12 34 3
4. N E S T S
   39 47 7 31 52
5. P L O T
   45 17 40 26
6. G H O S T
   24 14 43 32 8
7. F R E S H
   10 46 22 48 37
8. T H I G H
   51 2 23 29 41
9. S T A T E
   16 36 6 15 49
10. B O N E
   42 9 27 38
11. D E L A Y
   35 5 11 18 44

Solution to puzzle on page 56

STRONGMAN SAMSON

Solution to puzzle on page 57

Spring Festival

1. MEGILLOT
2. CONFIRMATION
3. REAPING
4. HARVEST
5. RUTH
6. NAOMI
7. MOABITE
8. FIRST FRUITS
9. DEVOTION
10. LOYALTY
11. BOAZ
12. SHAVUOT
13. CHAG SAMEACH

Solution to puzzle on page 58

Garden of Eden

W¹	H²	O³	■	D⁴	I⁵	D⁶	■	T⁷	H⁸	E⁹	■	W¹⁰	E¹¹	E¹²
D¹³	I¹⁴	N¹⁵	G¹⁶	■	I¹⁷	N¹⁸	■	T¹⁹	H²⁰	E²¹	■	G²²	A²³	R²⁴
D²⁵	E²⁶	N²⁷	■	O²⁸	F²⁹	■	E³⁰	D³¹	E³²	N³³	■	A³⁴	N³⁵	D³⁶
■	D³⁷	I³⁸	D³⁹	■	T⁴⁰	H⁴¹	E⁴²	Y⁴³	■	K⁴⁴	N⁴⁵	O⁴⁶	W⁴⁷	■
A⁴⁸	B⁴⁹	O⁵⁰	U⁵¹	T⁵²	■	M⁵³	I⁵⁴	R⁵⁵	A⁵⁶	C⁵⁷	L⁵⁸	E⁵⁹	■	G⁶⁰
R⁶¹	O⁶²	?	■											

1. W I D E
   10 54 36 26
2. T H A N K
   52 2 23 18 44
3. D A R E
   4 48 55 30
4. D A N
   39 56 35
5. O U T D I D
   28 51 19 25 14 37
6. B I G O T
   49 17 22 46 7
7. W O M E N
   1 50 53 12 33

8. D R E D G E
   13 61 9 31 60 42
9. O H I O
   62 20 38 3
10. H E E D
    41 32 21 6
11. E N C H A N T
    59 27 57 8 34 15 40
12. F L Y E R
    29 58 43 11 24
13. W I N G
    47 5 45 16

Solution to puzzle on page 59

The Fretting Prophet

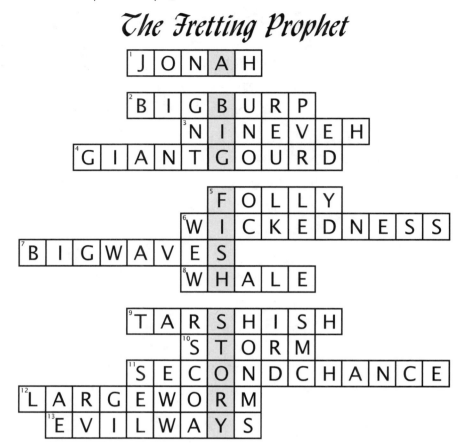

Solution to puzzle on page 60

DAY OF PENITENCE

1. KOL NIDRE
2. AL CHET
3. NEILA
4. CHARITY
5. YIZKOR
6. FASTING
7. ASHAMNU
8. KADDISH
9. ATONEMENT
10. MOURNING
11. REPENTANCE
12. CONFESSION
13. YOM KIPPUR

Solution to puzzle on page 61

Noah

¹A	²L	³L		⁴A	⁵N	⁶I	⁷M	⁸A	⁹L	¹⁰S		¹¹M	¹²A	¹³R
¹⁴C	¹⁵H		¹⁶I	¹⁷N		¹⁸T	¹⁹W	²⁰O		²¹B	²²Y		²³T	²⁴W
²⁵O		²⁶C	²⁷R	²⁸I	²⁹E	³⁰D		³¹N	³²O	³³A	³⁴H		³⁵J	³⁶O
³⁷I	³⁸N		³⁹O	⁴⁰U	⁴¹R		⁴²F	⁴³L	⁴⁴O	⁴⁵A	⁴⁶T	⁴⁷I	⁴⁸N	⁴⁹G
	⁵⁰Z	⁵¹O	⁵²O											

1. J A I L
   35 12 47 3
2. C O L O R
   14 51 9 36 27
3. M O N T H
   11 39 5 23 34
4. W O R N
   24 20 13 31
5. L I O N
   43 16 32 48
6. F O A M
   42 52 4 7
7. B O A
   21 25 45
8. Z I O N
   50 6 44 38
9. A C H E
   8 26 15 29
10. S T A I N
   10 46 33 28 17
11. G U I L T Y
   49 40 37 2 18 22
12. D R A W
   30 41 1 19

Solution to puzzle on page 62

FEAST OF LOTS

Down/Across crossword solution:

- ¹HAMANTASHEN
- ²PARTY
- ³PURIM
- ⁴GROGGERS
- ⁵OIL
- ⁶HAMAN
- ⁷VASHTI
- ⁸AHASUERUS
- ⁹HOLIDAY
- ¹⁰CARNIVAL
- ¹¹MORDECAI
- ¹²COSTUME
- ¹³MEGILLA
- ¹⁴ESTHER
- ¹⁵FAITH
- ADAR

Solution to puzzle on page 63

The First Boatbuilder

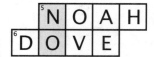

```
        ¹A R K
        ²O L I V E
      ³B R A N C H
        ⁴S H E M
```

```
        ⁵N O A H
      ⁶D O V E
```

```
    ⁷M O U N T A R A R A T
      ⁸A N I M A L S
      ⁹R A I N B O W
        ¹⁰F O R T Y D A Y S
      ¹¹J A P H E T H
          ¹²F L O O D
    ¹³R E P T I L E S
          ¹⁴H A M
    ¹⁵B I R D S
```

Solution to puzzle on page 64

Eternal City

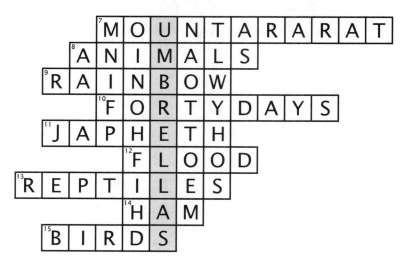

```
        ¹J U D A I C A
    ²M O U N T H E R Z L
    ³W E S T E R N W A L L
        ⁴S O U K
        ⁵C H A S S I D I M
        ⁶C H A G A L L W I N D O W S
      ⁷V I A D O L O R O S A
      ⁸M E A S H E A R I M
        ⁹D O M E O F T H E R O C K
```

```
      ¹⁰K N E S S E T
    ¹¹S H T R E I M L S
  ¹²D A M A S C U S G A T E
  ¹³H A D A S S A H H O S P I T A L
    ¹⁴D A V I D ' S T O M B
    ¹⁵Y A D V A S H E M
```

102

Solution to puzzle on page 65

SHOFAR TIME

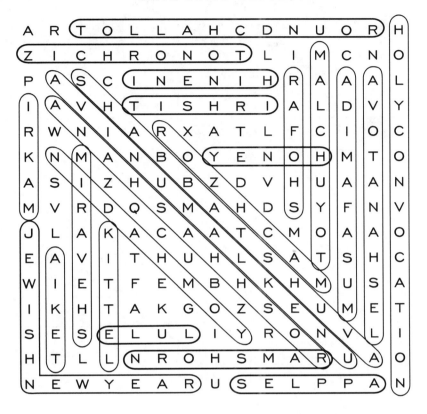

Solution to puzzle on page 66

THE TRIBES

1. JUDAH
2. EPHRAIM
3. MANASSEH
4. ISSACHAR
5. NAPHTALI
6. ZEBULUN
7. ASHER
8. GAD
9. REUBEN
10. DAN
11. SIMEON
12. BENJAMIN

Solution to puzzle on page 68

Bar Mitzvah

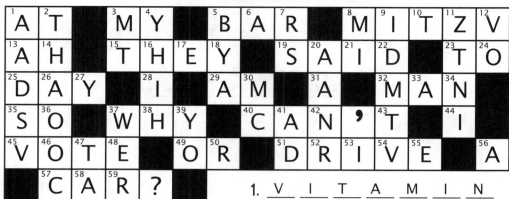

¹A	²T			³M	⁴Y			⁵B	⁶A	⁷R		⁸M	⁹I	¹⁰T	¹¹Z	¹²V
¹³A	¹⁴H		¹⁵T	¹⁶H	¹⁷E	¹⁸Y		¹⁹S	²⁰A	²¹I	²²D		²³T	²⁴O		
²⁵D	²⁶A	²⁷Y		²⁸I		²⁹A	³⁰M		³¹A		³²M	³³A	³⁴N			
³⁵S	³⁶O		³⁷W	³⁸H	³⁹Y		⁴⁰C	⁴¹A	⁴²N	⁴³'	⁴⁴T		⁴⁵I			
⁴⁵V	⁴⁶O	⁴⁷T	⁴⁸E		⁴⁹O	⁵⁰R		⁵¹D	⁵²R	⁵³I	⁵⁴V	⁵⁵E		⁵⁶A		
		⁵⁷C	⁵⁸A	⁵⁹R	?											

1. V I T A M I N
   12 44 47 1 30 21 34
2. Y A C H T
   4 29 57 38 15
3. C R A Z Y
   40 52 56 11 39
4. S H O V E
   35 14 24 45 55
5. D A I R Y
   22 31 53 7 18
6. W A I S T
   37 41 28 19 10
7. B O A T
   5 46 58 23
8. M A D A M
   32 26 51 13 3
9. A V I A T O R
   33 54 9 20 43 49 50
10. M O N E Y
   8 36 42 17 27
11. T H R E A D
   2 16 59 48 6 25

Solution to puzzle on page 67

Yom Kippur

| ¹A | L | I | Y | O | T | A | W | A | R | D | S |
| | | | | | ²N | E | I | L | A | | |

³T	A	L	I	T
⁴F	A	S	T	D	A	Y
⁵Y	I	Z	K	O	R

⁶S	E	L	F	D	E	N	I	A	L
	⁷K	O	L	N	I	D	R	E
	⁸T	O	R	A	H
	⁹R	I	G	H	T	E	O	U	S	N	E	S	S
¹⁰K	A	D	D	I	S	H
		¹¹V	O	W	S
¹²A	L	C	H	E	T
	¹³A	T	O	N	E	M	E	N	T
¹⁴A	B	S	T	I	N	E	N	C	E
		¹⁵A	S	H	A	M	N	U
¹⁶S	I	N	S

Solution to puzzle on page 69

Celebrating Rosh Hashana

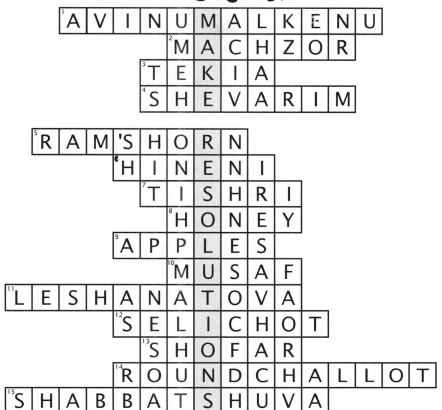

```
¹A V I N U M A L K E N U
   ²M A C H Z O R
   ³T E K I A
   ⁴S H E V A R I M
```

```
⁵R A M ' S H O R N
         ⁶H I N E N I
           ⁷T I S H R I
             ⁸H O N E Y
         ⁹A P P L E S
           ¹⁰M U S A F
⁹¹L E S H A N A T O V A
       ¹²S E L I C H O T
         ¹³S H O F A R
       ¹⁴R O U N D C H A L L O T
⁹⁵S H A B B A T S H U V A
```

Solution to puzzle on page 70

YIDDISH THEATRE STARS

Solution to puzzle on page 71

HAPPY NEW YEAR

1. AVINU MALKENU
2. LESHANA TOVA
3. MUSAF AMIDA
4. SHOFAR
5. ROUND CHALLOT
6. ZICHRONOT
7. HINENI
8. SHEVARIM
9. YOM HADIN
10. SHOFROT
11. TEKIA
12. MALCHUYOT
13. ROSH HASHANA

Solution to puzzle on page 72

FAMOUS ZIONISTS AND ISRAELIS

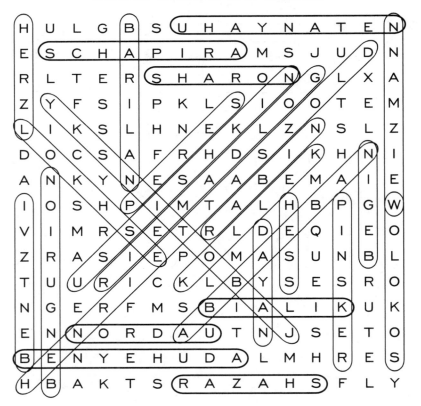

Solution to puzzle on page 73

Sabbath Peace

```
¹H A F T A R A
²L E C H A D O D I
³S P I C E B O X
```

```
⁴S H A L O M A L E I C H E M
         ⁵O N E G S H A B B A T
⁶K I D D U S H
   ⁷T A L I T
```

```
         ⁸H A V D A L A
      ⁹H A M O T Z I
¹⁰C A N D L E S
      ¹¹P R A Y E R S
```

```
      ¹²S I D D U R
         ¹³C H A L L A
            ¹⁴Y A R M U L K E
```

About the Authors

Sylvia Levinsohn, a former newspaper reporter, has been president of Poughkeepsie, New York's Temple Beth El Sisterhood and co-chairperson of its *First Sisterhood Cookbook* project. She is a past president of the Women's Division of the United Jewish Appeal, a former vice-president of Hadassah, and founder of the Mid-Hudson Chapter of the National Women's Committee for Brandeis University.

Arthur Levinsohn, a retired pharmacist, is a past president of Temple Beth El. As chairman of the temple's building committee, he was highly instrumental in seeing to completion the construction of its new synagogue. Mr. Levinsohn was active in the early promotion of Israel Bonds and is a former president of the UJA of Dutchess County.

Sylvia and Arthur Levinsohn were the 1992 honorees at the Dutchess County Annual Jewish Federation dinner. They have a son and a daughter and two granddaughters.

The Levinsohns' history of puzzle-making embraces several years of their double-crostics syndication by *The New York Times*, a year under the aegis of the Crossword Club, and the publication of *Current Crostics* (Quadrangle Press).